Introduction

Since the first tractors appeared on farms across the world, farmers have been keen to maximise the efficiencies offered by mechanisation. Getting their machines to work more effectively increased output and profitability.

Tractor manufacturers were quick to realise that they needed to continually evolve the products they offered, either by making them cheaper, more powerful or a combination of the two.

By the 1950s, very few horses remained on farms and tractors were the key to making farming more efficient. Globally, this took many forms – in Great Britain, the sub-30hp Ferguson TE-20 was ideal for the average farm, but large-acreage units needed something bigger, such as the Doe Dual Drive – two tractors joined together to produce around 100hp!

In Australia, where cropped areas were vast, tractor manufacturers built their machines with long hours in mind – equipped with large fuel tanks and substantial drawbar assemblies for hauling trailed implements in tandem across the land.

It was similar in the United States, with pioneering farmers using tractors in tandem to produce the desired output, but it would be the articulated, four-wheel drive monsters that would eventually rule the roost.

The mid-1950s saw Wagner emerge as a serious player in America's big tractor market and others would soon follow – such as Steiger and Versatile – with some making waves across the Atlantic, in Europe, too.

Climate and economy have a huge bearing on farming practices across the globe and so it is interesting to note how 'big' tractors differed on each continent. Quite often, a tractor built in the USA would appear on British farms, as the company's European wing could see how an overseas model might fill a gap in the market.

On the other hand, many European-based manufacturers would only consider designing tractors for their home market, as large-acreage prairie-type farms were considered the domain of the specialist tractor manufacturers.

In short, a 'big' tractor in Europe might be 100-150hp, while in Australia and the United States, 400-500hp would be considered large. As a result, this book covers tractors built from the early 1950s to the early 1990s across the globe – tractors that were deemed more suitable for larger farms.

It is worth remembering that 'the push for power' wasn't always about a big engine – traction, stability, power-to-weight ratio, weight distribution and running costs were all important factors when choosing the right tractor for the job.

Getting power to the ground has always been key; four-wheel drive is a distinct advantage, but some of the tractors featured here use dual, even triple wheels to gain extra grip, while reducing compaction. Tracks are also useful at transmitting power and have lower ground pressure too – so it's interesting to note that two of the machines in the book point toward what would become a resurgence in track-laying technology – a type of propulsion common on farms during the middle of the last century.

Many tractors in the book have a technical specification panel displaying useful statistics – but due to the diverse range of equipment featured, every entry in the book has a gold-coloured 'key facts' panel that provides at-a-glance information enabling the reader to quickly compare models.

Whatever your taste, there's something to interest everyone here – from tales of farmyard ingenuity to the vast research and development budgets of the major players in the tractor-building market. Despite their obvious differences, all of the machines in this book have one thing in common – they are responses to the desire of farmers worldwide to increase productivity. ∎

GREATEST TRACTORS - **The Push for Power**

Published by

KELSEY PUBLISHING GROUP

Printed in England, United Kingdom by William Gibbons
of Willenhall, West Midlands
on behalf of
Kelsey Publishing Limited,
Cudham Tithe Barn,
Cudham, Kent TN16 3AG
Telephone: 01959 541444   Fax: 01959 541400
www.kelsey.co.uk

©2011
ISBN 978-1-907426-18-6

With thanks to:
Dave Beare, Kim Jackson, Scott Lambert, Peter Love, Kim Parks,
Howard Sherren, Peter D Simpson, Frank Summerlin and Paul Tofield.
Also a big thank you to the owners of all the tractors featured.

Contents

6-7   American rarity
Scott Lambert takes a look at the lesser-known Wagner Tractormobile.

8-11   Which one is No.1?
Peter D Simpson unravels the mystery surrounding early Steigers.

12-15   Aboard a Triple 'D'
Dave Beare test drives the big one – the legendary Doe Dual Drive.

16-17   John Deere's dinosaur
Peter Love looks at JD's large 'New Generation' tractor.

18-19   Tandem two-stroke
We find a Chamberlain Super 70 outside Australia.

20-23   A massive flop
IH launched a 15-ton tractor in 1961, but why were only a few built?

24-27   Breaker turns maker
Kim Jackson goes to Preston to see a former scrap man's restoration.

28-29   The fabulous 5020
Frank Summerlin meets Peter Hill and his imported JD 5020.

30-33   The John Deere Wagner
Bruce Pester talks about his three JD Wagner tractors.

34-37   The sole survivor?
A tractor that many have never seen, or even heard of, before.

38-41   Wrexham revelation
An immaculate M-M A4T-1600 in North Wales is probably unique.

42-47   British powerhouse
We look in depth at a slice of UK history, the Massey Ferguson 1200.

48-51   Resting in peace
Muir-Hills are not common, but still out there as Kim Parks discovers.

52-55   Runaway rarity
A family saves a tractor from the scrapyard after a horrific accident.

56-57   Lonely existence
Farming in America can be lonely, as Joe Stringer knows too well.

58-60   The Rite tractor
Peter D Simpson takes a look at the history of the Rite tractor.

61-64 Zetor's magic Crystals
Members of the Daly family talk about their tractors.

65-68 Passion for big kit
Scott Thomas has six articulated tractors in his fleet.

69-72 A-C 'Queen Marys'
One of the last working A-C prairie tractors in New York State.

73-78 Ford's big beasts
Advice on buying one of Ford's FW Series tractors.

79-81 Farming in Montana
The Williams brothers tell us how tractor requirements have changed.

82-87 Supersize me
We look at the biggest Massey Ferguson tractors of them all.

88-93 Australian Colossus
One of the few high-horsepower tractors that is two-wheel drive.

94-98 Bomb-proof build
The rugged Favorit LS range was Fendt's answer to the competition.

99-101 Biggest of them all
One of the most powerful tractors in Europe is restored.

102-103 Built to last
The Versatile 895 – an over-engineered monster of the prairies.

104-109 The Italian Stallion
A Fiat 110-90 is easy to use, simple and reliable, says Howard Sherren.

110-115 Force II be reckoned with
We take a look at Ford's later, darker blue, TW Series tractors.

116-119 Caterpillars on rubber
Paul Tofield tells the story of the $100,000 Challenger.

120-121 Is it a Ford?
The Ford 976 appears to be very similar to other tractors.

122-125 End of the trac
Mercedes-Benz's MB trac was unique but was not to last.

126-129 First and last
An example of the last crawler range to leave Track-Marshall's factory.

This early Wagner TR-9 Tractormobile is believed to be the only one of its type in the United Kingdom. It features its original industrial-type tyres and is in remarkable condition for its age. Photo: Peter D Simpson.

American rarity

Scott Lambert takes a look at the lesser-known Tractormobile models built by Wagner Tractors.

Perhaps more famous for its John Deere-liveried machines, Wagner Tractor Inc's first agricultural offering was the TR Series ranging from 105-150hp. Introduced in 1954, the TR-6, TR-9 and TR-14 models were designed for heavy, general-purpose farm work and were powered by diesel engines, but petrol-power was available as an option.

With such construction machinery as the Mixermobile and Scoopmobile in its repertoire, Wagner opted to name its agricultural machine the Tractormobile. Using technology pioneered on its construction machines, such as the Pow-R-Flex drive coupling, Wagner was able to create a rugged four-wheel drive tractor with power steering and either eight (TR-6) or ten (TR-9 and TR-14) forward speeds.

Power was provide by Cummins four-stroke diesel engines; the six-cylinder JF-6-BU model in the TR-6, the four-cylinder NHCBI-400 in the TR-9 and the six-cylinder HBI-600 in the TR-14.

The TR-9, shown here, produced 390lb/ft of torque at 1,200rpm from its 495cu in engine and was good for 120hp. With a bore of 5⅛in and stroke of 6in, the Cummins unit had ample lugging ability and was the perfect match for the dual-range Fuller transmission, capable of 18mph on the road.

Weighing in at 14,600lb (6,622kg) the TR-9 was no lightweight, but manoeuvrability and control were good, with a turning radius of 9ft 4in (2,845mm) and axle oscillation of 18in (457mm) helping to keep all four wheels in contact with the ground at all times. In agricultural form (TR), the tractor's standard specification was basic – a single spool valve accompanied the drawbar-only rear end and single 15x26 wheels and tyres were all that was available to get power to the ground. Industrial models (TRS) featured wider tyres, an additional spool valve and a higher-capacity hydraulic pump for powering a dozer blade or scraper.

Although not the most technologically-advanced tractors, the TR Series put Wagner on the road to becoming a respected player in the four-wheel drive market. So much so, in fact, that the FWD Corporation decided to buy the company in 1961, creating FWD Wagner. The tractors lost their striking orange livery and became the WA Series, painted yellow.

At the end of the 1960s, John Deere entered into an arrangement with FWD Wagner to market the WA-14 and WA-17 models in its green and yellow colour scheme and it is believed that it was this that effectively sealed the end for FWD Wagner, as the terms of the agreement were such that the company wasn't allowed to produce models that would compete directly with those offered by Deere.

Despite the relatively small number of Wagner tractors produced, there are many still at work across America. Their rugged construction has helped them stand the test of time, making them a cheap source of power for those looking to pull implements across large fields. ■

Key facts

Built:	Minnesota, USA
Engine:	6-cyl Detroit Diesel
Power:	238hp
Chassis:	Articulated, four-wheel drive
Typical farm:	Large American arable

The big 238hp tractor, powered by a Detroit Diesel six-cylinder engine, is now housed at Bonanzaville museum, Fargo, North Dakota.

Which one is No.1?

Peter D Simpson unravels some of the mystery surrounding early Steigers.

Steiger is probably the greatest name in the world as far as big four-wheel drive articulated tractors are concerned. There are several details from the early days of Steiger tractor production that have caused some confusion both in America and the United Kingdom and I will try to explain some of those not-so-clear points.

I spent time with Steiger founder Douglas Steiger at his home and he explained to me the ins and outs of those early days.

When brothers Doug and Maurice Steiger, assisted by their father John, built that first tractor during the winter months of 1957/58 at their farm in Red Lake Falls, Minnesota, little did they know what the outcome would be.

Many people call this big 238hp tractor Steiger No.1 but in fact it isn't, this particular tractor has no official number at all, it was just another tractor built on a farm. Now

housed at Bonanzaville, Fargo, this big Steiger does, however, carry the designation No.1 on its descriptive board.

Some people think that Steiger was the first company to commercially produce four-wheel drive articulated tractors in America. The Wagner brothers started to produce these tractors in 1954 and on a large scale in 1956, with John Deere releasing its 8010 in the autumn of 1959.

Steiger tractor production commenced in 1961 after neighbouring farmers had pestered the Steiger brothers for several years to build them a tractor similar to the one they had built and were successfully using.

Steiger No.1 is, in fact, the first production Steiger, which was also built on the farm but much later, during 1961. The 1200, as it was called, only had a production run of three units even though some say that there were six 1200s built. The 1200 was powered by a six-cylinder Detroit Diesel engine producing 118hp.

This landmark tractor, Steiger No.1, has been saved and restored and is in the capable hands of father and son, Lloyd and Jeff Pierce in Minnesota, not many miles from where the tractor was first built. Lloyd purchased this tractor in 1961 and it has been in the family ever since.

There is a Steiger 1200 called No.4 in Bonanzaville, but this was the third 1200 and the fourth tractor built by the Steiger brothers. Nobody seems to know what happened to the second 1200, it may have been scrapped or it could be lying around the back of a barn somewhere.

Confused? I hope you aren't, as there is more to come. Jeff Pierce decided that a unique tractor collection could be built up if he could find one of each model of Steiger tractors built at Red Lake Falls.

So far he has achieved most of his ambition. He has restored the family's 1200 and has a 1250 with 130hp and a 2200 with 238hp running. He knows where there is a 318hp 3300 but has yet to find an example

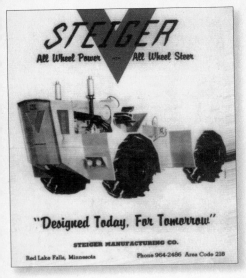

Above: Probably the earliest tractor sales brochure to come out of Red Lake Falls.

of the 195hp 1700. It will be a sad day if Jeff cannot complete this historic line-up.

For many years in agricultural engineering, manufacturers said there was an optimum power-to-weight ratio, which was in the region of 100lb weight to one horsepower. If you look at the numbering on these early Steigers, this rule applies.

Take the 300 for instance, at 318hp, multiply the horsepower by 100 and you have 31,800lb weight as the ideal. Near enough, the tractor weighed in at 33,00lb and was called the Steiger 3300.

There is another tractor that was built at Red Lake Falls that gets no mention in any tractor book and that is the logging tractor, the Logger 850, based on the 1250 agricultural tractor.

Above: Jeff Pierce drives Steiger No.1, which was bought new by his father, Lloyd, in 1961.

Right: A sales brochure for the Logger 850.

Despite popular belief that the brothers only built tractors in Euclid green, they also built several machines for the ➤

John Steiger tests a 1250 and set of trailed disc harrows that the brothers had altered to be used with such a tractor.

It was he who had seen high-horsepower machines on road construction jobs and thought why not have similar machines on the land instead of the 50-80hp tractors that were being used at the time. The 2200 construction machine had a factory-fitted front scraper and rear levelling bar, which could have ripper shanks fitted.

In 1969, an investor group bought into the small company to help it expand and tractor production subsequently moved from the farm to Fargo.

construction world. A construction-yellow 2200 model, fitted with a V6 Detroit Diesel engine, was put on to the market in the mid 1960s after Earl Christianson had joined the company as the sales and marketing manager.

Doug Steiger (left) and Earl Christianson.

Doug Steiger reminisces aboard Jeff Pierce's restored 2200 model.

A new line of tractors was introduced, which bore such names as Puma, Wildcat and Panther to name but a few. The Steiger name and its tractors travelled the world, becoming one of the most famous names in big-tractor history. ■

Dave Beare takes the controls of a Triple 'D'.

Aboard a Triple 'D'

Dave Beare test drives the big one – the legendary Doe Dual Drive.

Ernest Doe's production of tandem Fordson Majors in the late 1950s resulted from a small but persistent need for serious power and traction to pull multi-share ploughs through heavy soils, such as those in Essex and Lincolnshire.

The design was originated by Essex farmer George Pryor, who wanted around 100bhp and four-wheel drive, but could find nothing suitable on the market. Today 100bhp-plus 4x4 tractors are commonplace but 50 years ago nothing of the kind existed.

George Pryor's tandem tractor was a sensation and Ernest Doe soon became involved, as his company was the local Fordson dealership and probably supplied many of the parts that Pryor used.

The original George Pryor tractor needed a fair amount of re-engineering before it could be sold commercially since few of the controls were linked. For instance, changing gear on the front unit necessitated dismounting and using the original gear lever at the front, then remounting to drive off.

Doe was already producing a number of Fordson conversions and soon developed the necessary linked controls and improved some of the more rudimentary aspects of the Pryor tractor.

The Triple 'D', as it became known, was unique in 1958 in having 104bhp, tremendous traction and amazing manoeuvrability for its size. Despite being 19ft 9in long, the central articulation was nearly 90 degrees, enabling a Triple 'D' to turn virtually in its own length. At about 21

feet, the turning circle was five feet less than a standard Fordson Major.

It was, however, rather more complicated to drive as front and rear units still had some separate controls and drivers occasionally came to grief from lack of experience. It was also rather expensive – £2,350 for a Super Triple 'D' was big money for a tractor in the early 1960s.

This was rather less than a crawler capable of similar performance on heavy soil, such as a weighty 90bhp Caterpillar, which would have cost over £7,000, but a Doe was no lightweight, tipping the scales at 4.5 tonnes.

George Pryor and Ernest Doe's tractor was an instant success, with 289 built between 1958 and 1964, being exported all over the world.

A replacement, the 130bhp Doe 130, was introduced in 1965 and followed the same principles but used two more modern Ford 5000 skid-units. Progress soon caught up however; mainstream manufacturers brought out their own four-wheel drive tractors and economies of scale meant they were able to undercut the Doe 130 on price. Within a few years, Doe production ceased and the family business reverted to selling Ford tractors, an activity continued to this day by Ernest Doe's grandson, Colin Doe.

Triple 'D's were virtually hand-made on the Doe workshop floor. Large lumps of tractor were bought in from Ford, then modified in the welding and machine shops, using wherever possible readily-available parts such as the four steering-rams, which originated from Horndraulic loaders.

The centre turntable, with its four steering rams, was a stroke of genius. It allowed near-90-degree articulation whereas, with only two rams, a Triple 'D' would have had a huge turning circle and been cumbersome, unwieldy and unsuccessful.

Steering on a Triple 'D' is purely hydraulic; pressure is provided by a pump driven from the front crank pulley of the rear engine and supplied to a shuttle-valve connected to the steering wheel which operates two rams each side.

Gearing is high and, to anyone used to a normal Fordson Major, steering is feather-light and very direct.

View of a Triple 'D' from the driver's seat – the front unit's radiator surround is a long, long way away!

The standard Fordson clutch pedal of the rear unit is connected hydraulically via a balance-bar to two master and slave cylinders operating clutches in both units. Gear and ratio changing of the front unit is also achieved hydraulically. ➡

Ray Leach goes into a tight turn.

Key facts

Built:	Essex, UK
Engine:	2x 4-cyl Ford DDN-6003
Power:	2x 52hp
Chassis:	Articulated, four-wheel drive
Typical farm:	Large British arable

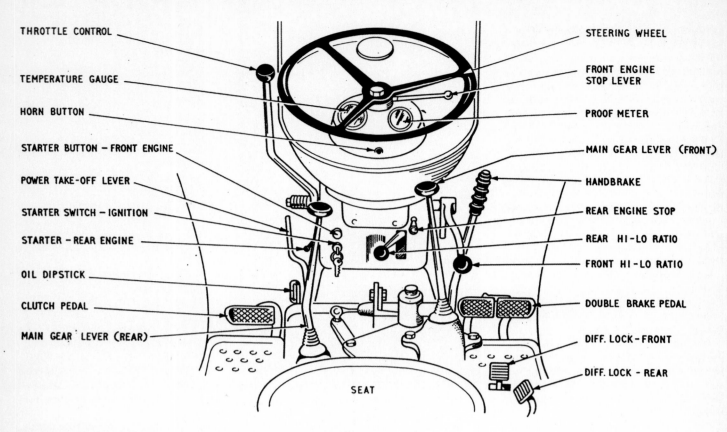

THROTTLE CONTROL	STEERING WHEEL
TEMPERATURE GAUGE	FRONT ENGINE STOP LEVER
HORN BUTTON	PROOF METER
STARTER BUTTON – FRONT ENGINE	MAIN GEAR LEVER (FRONT)
POWER TAKE-OFF LEVER	HANDBRAKE
STARTER SWITCH – IGNITION	REAR ENGINE STOP
STARTER – REAR ENGINE	REAR HI-LO RATIO
OIL DIPSTICK	FRONT HI-LO RATIO
CLUTCH PEDAL	DOUBLE BRAKE PEDAL
MAIN GEAR LEVER (REAR)	DIFF. LOCK-FRONT
	DIFF. LOCK - REAR

SEAT

View from the driving seat – a lot more controls than on a standard Fordson Major.

Two additional gear levers are fitted to the right side of the driver's seat, one controlling high/low ratios and the other main gear changing.

A series of small Lockheed hydraulic master cylinders transmits fore/aft and side-to-side motion from the rear-mounted lever to the front unit, where a steel box sits on top of what would be a Fordson gear lever.

A further series of identical hydraulic cylinders, attached to this, replicates motion from the rear lever to the front gearbox.

The two gearboxes are independently controlled so careful thought is needed before changing gear. The one thing not to do on a Doe is to end up with the front unit in reverse and the rear unit in first - a massive self-destruct follows!

It was quite common in use, however, to run the front unit in a higher forward gear than the rear to aid traction.

A new throttle control lever is mounted to the left of the steering wheel, which links both front and rear engines. They can be synchronised by adjusting link-rods, while the old Fordson throttle lever on the right side of the instrument binnacle now serves as the front engine stop-lever.

All this sounds very complicated but in practice it works well and, with practice, driving a Doe would become second-nature.

Enough of the technicalities: what is it like to drive?

I was given a cockpit drill by Ray Leach, owner of a magnificent 1959 Triple 'D' tractor that has been seen in action at many shows around Wales over the past few years, before he let me loose in a large field on the Llandysul showground.

First impression once you've climbed aboard and are seated comfortably – the front unit's radiator surround is a long, long way away!

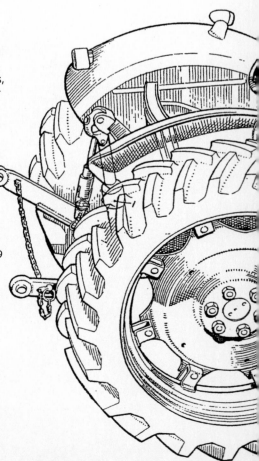

Left: Ernest Doe & Sons Ltd price list from the early 1960s. A Super Triple 'D' cost £2,350.

Right: Detailed drawing of the first Triple 'D', published in Farm Mechanisation magazine.

Both engines fire up instantly and tick over quietly; first gear of the front unit is engaged before the rear, Ray recommends lifting the clutch pedal gently until the front unit can just be felt pulling to ensure it is in gear.

The clutch pedal is then dipped again and the rear gear lever slotted into the same gear as the front. A few hundred revolutions per minute are added with the linked throttle control lever, the clutch pedal gently eased up and off we go.

It's immediately apparent that the steering has no feel whatsoever and is highly power-assisted. Any slight movement of the wheel and the vehicle reacts instantly: the front unit swings disconcertingly quickly and the first 20 yards are travelled in a series of long swerves.

Once one is accustomed to such instant changes of direction, the Triple 'D' is straightforward to drive although the proper sequence of gear-changing needs to be borne in mind at all times.

Turning on full lock is a revelation. It doesn't seem possible that such a long machine can turn within its own length but it can and the driver finds himself grinning from ear to ear as the front unit moves alongside him.

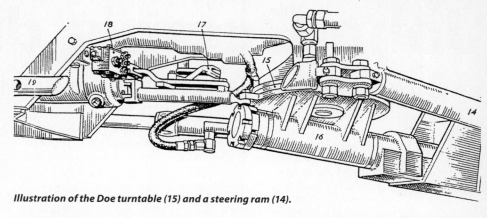

Illustration of the Doe turntable (15) and a steering ram (14).

One can only image what it must be like using a five or six-furrow plough behind a Triple 'D' with all that power and traction. No doubt this is why any Doe Dual Drive bought in for preservation needs considerable effort to return it to as-new condition: they were all worked to death!

Ray's Triple 'D' was delivered new to Lloyd Jenkins, of The Lodge, South Braithwaite, near Doncaster in South Yorkshire. It spent a few years ploughing the big arable fields of the area but was subsequently sold to

an unknown ploughing contractor on 17 February 1961.

From then on it worked long and hard until, thoroughly worn out, it was returned to Essex in the late 1990s as a virtual wreck.

Ray bought it as an unfinished project, has been working on it ever since and continues to do so. The quality of his restoration is superb and it was a real privilege to be allowed to drive a Triple 'D' – it was a day to remember. ■

John Deere's dinosaur

Peter Love looks at JD's large and advanced 'New Generation' tractor.

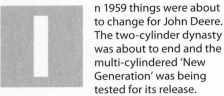

n 1959 things were about to change for John Deere. The two-cylinder dynasty was about to end and the multi-cylindered 'New Generation' was being tested for its release.

John Deere announced in Marshalltown, Iowa, in 1959 that it was introducing an 'eight-plow' four-wheel drive prairie tractor with a 200-horsepower engine, designated the 8010.

It was 19ft 7in long and 8ft 2in high, with power steering and air brakes. General Motors supplied a Detroit Diesel 6-71E two-stroke, six-cylinder engine, producing 215hp from its 425cu in displacement. The tractor produced 150hp at the drawbar, incredible for the time, channelling the power through a nine-speed transmission.

Unlike other such tractors of the period, it wasn't just built for pulling and featured a three-point linkage.

In field tests the combination proved unreliable, but the engineers knew that they were breaking new technology and Deere gave the go-ahead for the production run. They knew they weren't going to sell millions of tractors, but a few thousand would do. In the first year, they sold just one!

The major faults were the clutch and transmission, as they were not up to the job and regularly broke! All but one of the fifty 8010s were recalled under warranty and a new style of clutch and transmission was fitted, along with various other modifications.

These tractors were re-tagged the 8020, but they still did not sell well and it is suggested that it took seven years to clear all of the stock – a nightmare come true for John Deere. ■

John Deere's 8010 certainly looked impressive, but failed to meet many farmers' expectations.

Key facts

Built:	Iowa, USA
Engine:	6-cyl Detroit Diesel 6-71E
Power:	215hp
Chassis:	Articulated, four-wheel drive
Typical farm:	Large American arable

Tandem two-stroke

The Australian Chamberlain Super 70 is a rare bird outside its homeland, particularly in tandem configuration, but Scott Lambert managed to track one down that belongs to an enthusiast in the United Kingdom.

Built from 1954-62 in Welshpool, Western Australia, the Chamberlain Super 70 quickly gained a foothold in its homeland and became one of the company's most well-liked and well-respected models.

Powered by a Detroit Diesel 3-71, two-stroke diesel engine, the Super 70 had more than enough power to cope with whatever the large acreages threw in its direction.

Those of you that are familiar with the three-cylinder, supercharged unit will know that it has plenty of torque, but is not the quietest engine ever produced – in fact, it has been said that it is the most efficient

engine at turning fuel into noise! This aside, the 213cu in motor's 4¼in bore and 5in stroke combine to produce 77hp at the belt and 70hp at the drawbar – not to be sniffed at in the mid-1950s.

Equipped with a 9-forward, 3-reverse speed transmission (channelled through three ranges), the Super 70 was very effective at putting the power to the ground.

The tandem Super 70 stands out from the crowd in more ways than one. The sheer scale of the tractor is phenomenal, but coupled with the orange livery it is a real eye-catcher.

Produced:	1954-1962
Engine:	Detroit Diesel 3-71
Cylinders:	3 supercharged
Bore x stroke:	4¼in x 5in
Displacement:	213cu in
Horsepower:	77hp
Rated speed:	1,500rpm
Transmission:	9 forward, 3 reverse
Speed range:	3⅛mph – 18¾mph
Linkage:	Drawbar only
Hydraulics:	7.7gpm pump, 1,000psi
Weight:	11,000lb (with ballasted dual rear tyres, fuel and oil)
Tyre sizes:	Front: 8.25x20
	Rear: 18x26 singles or 13.5x32 duals

The Super 70 was designed as a drawbar-only machine, for pulling large implements.

Note: Data shown is for standard Chamberlain Super 70 tractor, not tandem model shown here.

Key facts

Built:	Western Australia
Engine:	2x 3-cyl Detroit Diesel 3-71
Power:	2x 77hp
Chassis:	Articulated, four-wheel drive
Typical farm:	Large Australian arable

In standard guise, 18x26 rear tyres were big enough to turn power into pull, but many operators opted to use ballasted 13.5x32 duals to aid traction. This all changed when two tractors were coupled together, such as the machine shown here, with phenomenal amounts of pull able to be achieved from the drawbar.

Just as Ernest Doe had successfully achieved in England, Australian farmers and manufacturers had managed to mate two tractors together to double the power of their workhorses. This was often rather rudimentary – nothing more than one tractor fitted to the drawbar of another, but other offerings were much more professional.

Like a Triple 'D', a tandem Super 70 was designed with the forward-thinking farmer in mind. It was suited to those that had a lot of work to do and needed a tractor that could cope with anything they asked of it.

The tractor here is probably somewhere between the two, in that a nicely-crafted turntable arrangement is present, but not all functions can be controlled from the driver's seat on the rear unit. For example, a hand-operated clutch provides the control for both units, but the driver has to dismount and select the desired gear on the front unit before engaging gear on the rear unit and moving off.

In Australia, where vast acreages were covered by tractors every day, this was obviously not deemed to be a problem and drivers just got on with it – after all, pulling a massive disc plough or stubble cultivator across a huge field meant that the operator rarely changed gear.

The Super 70 was only offered with a drawbar and 540rpm pto, but had a substantial 7.7gpm hydraulic pump to operate the remote cylinders on the implements that it pulled.

Seeing one 'in the metal' won't be easy, but if you do have the opportunity to experience a Super 70 (either in standard or tandem form) – savour the moment, as it's certainly one that will be etched in your mind forever! ■

The Detroit Diesel 3-71 two-stroke, three-cylinder engine was supercharged, producing 77hp.

A massive flop

International Harvester launched a 15-ton tractor in 1961, but only a few were built. Howard Sherren explains why.

The large, articulated tractor market was dominated by manufacturers such as Wagner and John Deere in the early 1960s, but International Harvester saw a hole in the market and launched the 4300 in 1961.

It was the first tractor to be offered with a turbo and unique features such as three-way steering, four-wheel-drive and an impressive engine. At the time there was growing demand for high-powered tractors.

The 4300 was mainly aimed at the large farms on the Great Plains in the US. Painted bright yellow, it was easily identifiable and its connection with the industrial division of

IH clearly showed, although it was built by Frank G. Hough Co. in Lerbtyville, Illinois.

International had started playing with the concept of a big, equal-wheel, four-wheel drive tractor in late 1957. It was renowned for its wheeled loaders and its experience in

The 4300's striking yellow colour was to show its connection with Hough, the industrial side of IH. An early prototype was painted red and white.

The massive 817cu in IH DT-817 engine produced 300hp at the flywheel.

Key facts

Built:	Illinois, USA
Engine:	6-cyl IH DT-817
Power:	300hp
Chassis:	Rigid, four-wheel drive
Typical farm:	Large American arable

this market was used to develop this rigid-frame concept – and may have helped it not infringe Wagner's design patent.

The first prototype was completed in 1959, dubbed the 4-WD-1 and painted red with white bars on the grille to match the other models in IH's range. It featured two oscillating axles, which gave front-wheel, four-wheel, crab and independent steering.

At 125-150hp, it was decided it would not have enough power to compete with the likes of John Deere's 200hp 8010 model and just a year later the third and final prototype, 4-WD-3, was built with the new IH DT-817 engine and 180 drawbar horsepower, much more than before. The engine was also rated at up to 300hp, so was more than man enough for the job.

This was set to be the production 4300 and, using Hough axles, the tractor weighed in at 15 tons, ideal to get the traction required for most operations.

In the design process, the need for creep gears came to light and had to be considered. The original plan was to fit an agricultural eight-speed, sliding-gear transmission or an automatic transmission with a lockable torque converter as an option. The manual idea was rejected after a few complications and the automatic system was chosen.

A six-speed Allison CLBT 4460 Series transmission was manufactured especially for this new model and was hitched to a lockable torque converter to give a wide range of speeds.

The 1200psi hydraulic system was supplied by a 55 gallon per minute pump, driven by the engine. The steering system had a 15psi preference over other services, such as brakes and implements, making sure it would never be starved of oil.

In May 1961 the tractor went into production, badged as the International 4300 and painted in bright yellow livery. It featured multiple selling points over the competition – higher fuel efficiency, faster, easier and safer transport to and from the field, fully-pressurised cab with air conditioning and heaters, suspension seat, power steering and air brakes.

The 4300 was marketed as "the most powerful four-wheel-drive tractor in the world" and made much of its high-speed capabilities and high outputs. The tractor could easily handle a 10- or 12-furrow plough or cover up to 30 acres an hour with a 40ft chisel plough but, depending on the source you use, it appears that just 44 of these innovative tractors were produced and sold.

Just six are believed to have made it on to big farms: the rest went on to construction sites, pulling scrapers or water tanks, to which they were more suited. The torque converter transmission worked well in loaders but for agricultural use it was less efficient. When pulling implements, a ➡

A Bendix-Westinghouse two-cylinder, engine-driven compressor supplied air to the tractor's brakes.

International Harvester's production literature for the 4300 and earlier 4-WD-3 models.

tractor is likely to spend most of its time working at maximum torque, so a converter increased fuel consumption and reduced the transmission's service life.

There are thought to have been three main reasons for the model's failure: firstly that the horsepower of the tractor was too big a jump for the rubber-tyred tractor market, secondly that IH had no implements to use all the power and lastly that it was difficult for IH to sell products across divisions. Company politics meant that the discussion of the 4300 project with engineers from the agricultural division to perfect the design was near impossible. The 4300 was found in agricultural literature some two years after production ceased in 1965 but little interest was shown.

In the end, perhaps the 4300 was ahead of its time and so met a similar fate to John Deere's 8010 and 8020 tractors. IH succeeded though when they launched their next 'practical' four-wheel-drive, the 4100 in 1966. This sold in the region of 1,200 units in its two-year production run.

Engine
The production model used International's new IH DT-817 six-cylinder diesel turbo engine to propel the monster of a tractor. It had an impressive 817cu in displacement, a 180kg crankshaft, 146mm bore and 152mm stroke. Wet-type replaceable sleeves gave better serviceability in the future.

In a Nebraska test, the tractor showed 214hp at the drawbar and as much as 300hp at the flywheel. This was much more than anything else around at the time. The rated governed speed ranged from a typical 650rpm to a maximum of 2,100rpm. Maximum torque was found to be 825lb/ft at 1,500rpm. A 600-litre fuel tank provided enough capacity to keep that huge power unit running all day.

Transmission
The chosen Allison CLBT 4460 transmission was connected to a heavy-duty single-stage, polyphase, three-element torque converter. This enabled the tractor to set off in any gear, which was useful, but not fuel efficient

or good for the life of the converter. The transmission offered six forward gears.

With torque converter locked, the four working speeds were 3½, 5, 7¼ and 10¼mph. Two extra transport speeds of 14½ and 20½mph were available to reduce travelling time and increase the 4300's versatility. The transmission split drive to front and rear axles, keeping the power equal across the tractor.

Rear linkage
Although a heavy-duty category IV three-point linkage was offered in the sales literature, a hydraulically-adjustable drawbar was fitted in most cases. A swinging drawbar was connected to two hydraulic rams, giving it the ability to be raised and lowered. This proved useful as most equipment at the time was trailed, but there weren't many implements designed for the 4300.

Two 10-furrow ploughs were supposedly produced for demonstration purposes, but special toolbars known as "squadron hitches" were more common. This was where multiple implements were joined to utilise the tractor's power. "Combination hook-ups" - where three or four drills were hooked up together to get increased width – were also suggested.

Hydraulics
Surprisingly, the 4300 came with two separate hydraulic systems running at 40gpm. One system was used exclusively for the steering system, while the second fed several different circuits in the implement system. A 55gpm pump was optional for extra output. Three spools were standard with automatic return and one had a float position.

Axles & brakes
Hough FS 100 live steering axles were used to steer and manoeuvre the tractor. This axle featured 3.7:1 ring and pinion reduction in the centre section and 5.2:1 reduction in the planetary hubs. This meant the final reduction ratio came to 19.2:1.

The three-way steering system provided a two-wheel steer option, intended for highway travel or those very long runs while working in the field. Then four-wheel steer and crab steer provided more versatility in the field. In 4WS, the turning circle was

A quantity of simple analogue dials and range of levers made the 4300 straightforward to use.

Gear selection is via this interesting, and possibly awkward, lever and gate.

Three spools were standard and the long levers were not much of a stretch to reach.

Technical specification

Engine:	IH DT-817
Horsepower:	300hp
Maximum power @:	2,100rpm
Maximum torque @:	1,500rpm
Cylinders:	6 turbocharged
Bore x stroke:	146mm x 152mm
Displacement:	817cu in
Fuel capacity:	600 litres
Transmission:	8 forward, 1 reverse Allison torque converter
Turning radius:	5,200mm
Length:	6,600mm
Width:	2,820mm
Weight:	15,000kg
Tyre sizes:	23.1 R26

reduced from 9.4m to just 5.2m – ideal for tighter headland turns.

The crab-steer option was also particularly useful on steep banks where a straight line was to be maintained. Originally the tractor came on 23.1x26 12-ply tyres, but 23.5x25 earthmover tyres or 26.5 25 semi-agricultural tyres were an option.

Brakes were a very important factor when it came to designing a 15-ton monster like this. A 20½in diameter by 4in expanding drum-type brake on each wheel was responsible for slowing the enormous tractor. Actuation was thanks to air supplied by a Bendix-Westinghouse two-cylinder, engine-driven compressor. A single cable-actuated brake on the output shaft of the transmission acted as a park and emergency brake.

Cab

A fully-enclosed cab was available as an optional extra. The pressurised and climate-controlled cab came with air conditioning and a heater, which were luxury options in that era.

The IH 4300 was first put into production in May 1961 and created a lot of interest, but sadly only 44 were built. This particular tractor belongs to Nathan and Mat Swenson of Minot, North Dakota.

A leather, fully-adjustable seat was well positioned and many controls were relatively easy to reach. The cab also featured sliding side and fold-out rear windows, windscreen wipers and a cigarette lighter.

Power steering and air brakes made it a comfort to drive. It is unusual now to find a cabbed International Harvester 4300 due to the additional cost it put on the already expensive price tag. ■

The steering selector gave a straightforward option of any of the three steering modes.

The rear platform could be used for extra weight or carrying extra seed when drilling.

This restored cab-less 4300 belongs to Jerry Mez from Iowa.

Breaker turns maker

Kim Jackson heads for Preston to see a former scrap man's restoration.

At any tractor event the chances are that you will see a Fordson Major. People will stop and show interest but not to the same level as with a four-wheel drive Roadless, which is often the star of the show. Roadless tractors are highly regarded, even though they belong only to a small but growing band of enthusiasts dedicated to Roadless conversions.

David Kerrigan, from near Preston in Lancashire, is one such tractor collector. He has always been familiar with Fordsons: his father was a scrap dealer and broke many tractors but especially Fordsons. Indeed it was a Fordson Major which David first drove at the age of seven – "I could stand on the clutch, but was too small to sit on the seat."

More than 60 Standard Ns and 100 E27Ns were broken by the business in 45 years and from this came David's love of tractors. For the last 13 years he has been building up a specialist collection in which the Roadless marque predominates.

His sixth tractor restoration is a 1964 Ploughmaster 6/4, which was the first six-cylinder, four-wheel drive tractor Roadless conversion based on a Fordson Major.

The Roadless Major, launched in 1956, was essentially a conversion of a two-wheel drive Fordson Major to four-wheel drive by driving the front axle from a transfer case sandwiched between the gearbox and differential housing.

Then, in 1962, the Ploughmaster 6/4 arrived. This model was a more ambitious conversion and only 200 of them left Roadless Traction Ltd, of Hounslow, so it was a rare tractor to buy then and is even rarer in preservation.

Key facts

Built:	Middlesex, UK
Engine:	6-cyl Ford 590E
Power:	75hp
Chassis:	Rigid, four-wheel drive
Typical farm:	Large British arable

The tractor is shod with Firestone Traction Field & Road tyres, specially imported from the USA.

Half the production went abroad (a low percentage in the 1960s for an English tractor). Of those remaining, over half are believed to have survived. David's tractor is 6D3035-3 (axle number) and 5347784 (engine number).

Colchester Tractors, a subsidiary of Ernest Doe & Sons, registered it on 4 April 1964. It was the last one to be sold in the UK; the next 20 Ploughmaster 6/4s went to Mexico.

The tractor's history is largely unknown – the original registration details have gone missing and the Roadless has been issued with an age-related Preston plate.

David bought it from Richard Pocock, of Dorset, in 2004 and it remained at the back of his shed for two years before he had the time, money and energy to restore it.

Operating heavy plant for a living – a demanding six day-a-week job – tractor restoration for him is very much an enjoyable hobby.

When David bought the Roadless it was in a far different state to what it is today. Although the hour meter had stopped, it was obvious the tractor had had a full working life, it is thought principally ploughing. This is because as well as being designed for this most necessary and laborious job, the only gear to be worn out was second high.

Left: A new set of injectors was fitted to the 590E engine. The injection pump now works well after being fully reconditioned.

Over the years, parts had been stuck on the tractor – anything to keep it working – the paintwork showed blue, black and grey parts, it had the wrong exhaust and the wrong headlights. According to David: "Nearly everything was wrong."

When it was time to start the restoration David took the tractor apart and then decided to carry out the engine work first. The 590E six-cylinder Thames Ford Industrial engine had a complete overhaul because although the tractor was still running, the engine was worn out.

The pistons were re-ringed and the liners replaced. The crankshaft journals were polished and a set of new big end and main bearings purchased.

After the head had been skimmed, new valve guides were added before the engine was re-assembled.

The gearbox bearings were worn, as well as the aforementioned high second gear, and these were replaced. The oil pump was still in good condition but, to make sure everything was perfect, David fitted a new relief valve and rebuilt it.

A complete new clutch was needed; first the flywheel was skimmed and then the new pressure plate and driven plate added. David next overhauled the injection pump. The head received six new injectors. The water pump, starter motor and dynamo were thought beyond repair and new ones were fitted.

All 16 oil seals around the tractor were changed as well as the hydraulic top seal. The hydraulic pump itself was in good condition; to make sure it was tested with a pressure clock.

David did not carry out all the work; some was outsourced to local specialists. A lot of the engineering, including work on the three-point linkage and pick-up hitch, was carried out by Jeff Hollywell, of Holly Products, Mawdesley. ➡

At the heart of the conversion is the GMC front axle from a six-wheel drive, two-and-a-half tonne truck which has been narrowed by shortening the right-hand axle tube and half shaft.

To make the tractor a little bit more special, David acquired a raised pto kit and added it.

AK Hydraulics sorted out the power steering; to do this the internal valves on the power steering ram needed to be set up on a test rig.

When the tractor left the Ford plant it would have been fitted, as a two-wheel drive New Performance Super Major, with a fixed front axle. Roadless Traction substituted this with a front axle, which had once been destined for a General Motors 6x6 war-time truck but was now modified by shortening one axle tube and half shaft, as pioneered by Selene in Italy.

To get David's Ploughmaster front axle back to pristine condition it needed a complete differential and two new half shafts, which in the end were good, reconditioned second-hand ones. When assembled, nine new bearings were required in the axle, along with new wiper seals and felts. The brand new aspherical bearings were made by the same company that had made them in 1964.

The propshaft was also rebuilt, as was its multi-plate clutch, which was sent for reconditioning to Paul Bint, who incidentally owns an early Ploughmaster that was painted yellow and green in the style of John Deere. Paul fitted new bushes, a new shear pin and seals to make the clutch as good as new.

David refurbished the brakes himself, fitting new brake linings and a new pedal shaft for the brake pedals. The exhaust, which wasn't the correct one, was very corroded and a new one was sourced from the Old Twenty Parts Company.

Where possible David uses genuine parts. Most of the Ford ones came from Sparex via Ken Woodburn, a local agricultural mechanic, who also helped David with some of the Ploughmaster rebuild. The Roadless parts were sourced from Dave Pantry who was, at the time, the only specialist stockist of Roadless parts.

Now it was time for the facelift. Forty years of hard work had taken their toll on the tractor's looks. A new steering wheel was put in place, one of the last to leave Dagenham.

After David had sand blasted all the tin, the vehicle went to Frank Halsall, of F&J Halsall Plox Motors, for full cosmetic treatment. Frank knocked out the dents, filled all the minor imperfections, primed and then painted the panels with two-pack paint.

David is particularly pleased with the front nose cone; it is a genuine Ford part and it came via Richard Pocock from a dealer in Canada. Its lights are new and are genuine Butler ones, which David picked up some years ago thinking he might have a use for them one day.

He turned for the front chaff screens to Colin Perryman, who makes reproduction parts, and to Dunlop tractor spares for the wiring harnesses. The Roadless was upgraded with a Rest-a-ride seat – originally

Above: Despite Roadless Traction's roots in Hounslow, the axle serial number plate clearly shows the conversion has Italian origins.

Right: Roadless Ploughmaster 6/4 tractors were built for hard work and, as a large percentage of the 200 built have survived, it is a proof that it was well regarded as a working tool.

it was supplied with a metal pan seat but the deluxe seat was offered as an option.

The 6/4 is finished off very nicely with a set of refurbished mudguards. These were a lucky find: David saw them for sale in *Tractor & Machinery* as the original owner had fitted a Lambourn cab on a Fordson Super Major.

The tyres came from America – the Roadless was re-shod with Firestones. These were made to the pattern of its original tyres and are only made to order. David placed the order with the British Rubber Company and it set him back £1,140.

David sprayed the skid unit and all the ancillary parts, which were not panels (Frank Halsall did the bonnet and mudguards) and says that painting the tractor as soon as the repairs were completed was principally to save time, but it was not always for the best.

Once assembled, a couple of oil leaks were found, which would have been a lot easier to deal with if the tractor hadn't had its top coat of paint on. They have now been solved and the damage to the paintwork completely eradicated as well. In future, although much more time consuming, David thinks he will run a rebuilt tractor to see if there are any faults, dismantle it, then paint it before reassembling it.

Paint at £127 a gallon like that needed for most parts of the Ploughmaster is an expensive component. About one gallon of grey and two of Ford Empire blue were needed plus the activator and the gallon of red primer which went on first. The paint came from LPP at Preston who matched the paint colour exactly from un-faded samples that David saved.

The tractor's colour scheme may surprise some people. Roadless tractors are thought of as being blue, although most enthusiasts are aware of some of the early Ploughmaster 6/4 tractors carrying a green and yellow livery which set a certain "Deer" from Moline, Illinois, leaping.

Since there was no clear indication on David's tractor as to which colour it originally was, Dave Pantry was approached and David learned that his tractor was part of a consignment of 21 Ploughmasters ordered for delivery to Mexico – but for some reason David's was sold in Essex.

The usual export colour scheme was grey and blue: that is what went on David's tractor in 1964 and that is what David has replicated in 2007.

He spent the best part of a year to achieve a very comprehensive restoration of a Roadless Ploughmaster 6/4. It cost him over £13,000 in parts and for work he sourced out; his time is not been accounted for in this sum.

He is now looking forward to restoring his next tractor! ■

The fabulous 5020

Frank Summerlin meets Peter Hill and his imported John Deere 5020.

Peter Hill, from Northants, acquired his 1967 John Deere 5020 tractor in 2004 to team up with his first challenging restoration project, a John Deere 245H semi-mounted, seven-furrow plough.

The plough was originally supplied with a new John Deere 5010 to a nearby farm where it had been out of use for many years until Peter recovered it.

After struggling with rusted bolts and the like, as well as acquiring some new parts, the seven-furrow plough was returned to working condition.

As the 245H plough was designed for on-land working, the 5020 tractor fitted the bill admirably.

Although this tractor is an imported model, it does have a three-point linkage fitted – many 5020s were only sold with swinging drawbars and remote cylinder controls.

A clear exhaust as seven 16" furrows bite into the soil.

John Deere 5020 basic specification (UK): 1967

143hp six-cylinder engine
531cu in displacement
8 forward, 3 reverse synchro transmission
Power steering
Differential lock
Pre-cleaner with air stack
11.00x16 8-ply front tyres
24.5x32 10-ply rear tyres
Fixed-tread front axle 69" or 70" centres,
Rear wheels adjustable from 70"-91" centres
Twin headlights
Two combined work/red warning lights
Two remote cylinder control valves

Category II/III three-point linkage
1,000rpm pto
Quick coupler
Two front weights (85lb each)
Pair of side weights (88lb each)
Inner rear wheel weights (1,600lb each)
Pair of outer rear wheel weights (115lb each)

Price:
£5,643-0-0 (1 Dec 1967)

Factory installed options:
Adjustable front axle with 68", 72", 76" and

80" centres: £23-0-0

**Implements available in the UK for 5010/
5020 tractors (1967):**
The 245H plough with 7 x 16" cut furrows:
£1,180-0-0
24C toolbar: £196-0-0
Subsoil legs: £35-10-0 each
100F Series flexible trailed chisel plough –
24ft version & 24 cushion standards:
£1,210-0-0
C10 mounted cultivator 18½ft, 6" spacings:
£357-0-0

Key facts

Built:	Iowa, USA
Engine:	6-cyl John Deere 531cu in
Power:	143hp
Chassis:	Rigid, two-wheel drive
Typical farm:	American arable

Above: The width of the tractor and plough are shown off to advantage in this view.

Below: A powerful-looking beast if ever there was one. ■

The John Deere Wagner

Peter D Simpson meets Bruce Pester and his three JD Wagner tractors.

The John Deere Wagner WA-14 and WA-17 four-wheel drive articulated tractors are somewhat of a mystery to many enthusiasts, including John Deere personnel. The green John Deere Wagners are little recognised, they do not fit into the Wagner history, nor the John Deere history; they are classed by some as orphans.

The recorded history of these tractors is limited, often being misreported; yet they are a very important part of American big tractor history.

Less than 100 John Deere Wagner tractors were built and to find one still at work is a difficult job. As soon as one of these green giants appears on the market they are quickly snapped up by enthusiasts, who either restore them or put them to work along with other classics they own, namely the yellow Wagner tractors.

During the mid 1950s, John Deere management and the design team had been looking at ways of increasing tractor horsepower. They had conducted many tests on various tractors including the competition's powerful Case LA powered by a 3-71 General Motors engine, proving that higher power was the only way forward and that there was a growing market for tractors with considerably more power, size and weight.

Wayne H Worthington, John Deere's director of research, was convinced that to increase and utilise more power, the way ahead was with a four-wheel drive tractor and like the Wagner tractor, it should be articulated.

The team carried out further tests until they had an experimental two-wheel drive 150hp tractor ready, but it failed in every comparison test against a four-wheel drive articulated Wagner TR-14 tractor of similar power.

Worthington presented his findings to the various John Deere company directors, inviting them to observe for themselves several field tests between the two types of tractors. The result was that the directors gave immediate permission and funding for a John Deere-built four-wheel drive articulated tractor.

By the spring of 1958 the first big John Deere 8010, or 'eighty ten' as it was called, was undergoing field evaluation and was announced to an unsuspecting John Deere two-cylinder following at Marshalltown, Iowa in the fall of 1959.

This 1969 John Deere Wagner WA-14 was the first Wagner built tractor for John Deere in JD colours, serial number John Deere WA-14 000101.

Key facts

Built:	Oregon, USA
Engine:	6-cyl Cummins N855
Power:	225hp
Chassis:	Articulated, four-wheel drive
Typical farm:	Large American arable

After many problems with the big tractors, described as too big and too soon, John Deere ceased production of big four-wheel drive articulated tractors in 1964. The company had lost a lot of money on these big machines; it had learned a lot and started designing a completely-new type of four-wheel drive articulated tractor.

In the meantime the company could see Steiger and Versatile beginning to make inroads into the big tractor market and it needed something to fill the gap before its new tractor was ready.

On New Year's Eve 1968, John Deere and FWD Wagner signed a deal that entitled John Deere to the rights to the WA-14 and WA-17 tractors. Wagner would supply 100 tractors and John Deere would supply the decals and paint the tractors in its colours.

The two green John Deere Wagner models were virtually identical to each other, very similar to the previous yellow tractors; the only visible differences were colour, decals, tyre size, slight tin work and chassis modifications.

The engines fitted in to these machines were Cummins N855 engines that were naturally aspirated in the WA-14 and turbocharged in the WA-17 model. Most WA-14s were dealer turbocharged to 280hp at a later date.

John Deere's description of its new tractors was as follows: "They're big – they're powerful – and they're FAST. They're the new John Deere 225hp WA-14 and 280hp WA-17 Four-Wheel-Drive Tractors. Here's a combination of pull power, speed and ease of operation that will delight any large-acreage farmer seeking a sure-fire aid to help spread the cost-price squeeze. Either model paves the way for one man to increase the results of his individual efforts."

Powered by Cummins six-cylinder engines, fitted with Fuller Road Ranger RTO-910 transmissions giving 10 forward speeds and equipped with air brakes, the John Deere Wagner tractors were ideal for the large wheat farms of the northern states that required high power, giving great traction with minimal wheel slip for a straight drawbar pull.

The John Deere Wagner agreement lasted less than three years with fewer than the expected 100 tractors being ordered; in all there were 23 JD WA-14s and 28 of the JD WA-17s sold.

As part of the marketing agreement between the two companies it was specified that if John Deere stopped buying ⇒

Right: The easily-accessible Cummins N855 six-cylinder engine was naturally aspirated on the WA-14, producing 225hp. Most models were dealer turbocharged at a later date giving an extra 55hp. This engine has done 13,000 hours, with a major overhaul carried out at 7,000 hours.

tractors from Wagner, then Wagner could not produce a competing four-wheel drive articulated tractor for five years.

With this exclusive deal between the two companies, basically all yellow Wagner tractor production ended on New Years Eve 1968. John Deere introduced its new tractors, the 7020 and 7520, in 1971 and 1972 respectively.

While in Montana a few years ago, I was fortunate enough to come across a farmer east of Great Falls who owns and operates three of these green giants.

Bruce Pester farms 5,000 acres of arable and grassland and says the John Deere Wagner tractors are ideal for his farming operation and he just loves the nostalgia these tractors bring to the farm.

Bruce started farming on his own during 1978 with a lease 60 miles south of Chinook, Montana near the Fort Belnap Indian reservation. He married Melinda in 1985 after they both graduated from Montana State University in 1984 and they moved to their present farmstead at Lewistown, Montana shortly after.

The B Bar M Ranch is non-irrigated, relying on an average annual precipitation of 20 inches with 110 frost-free days. Most precipitation is received in the winter months into late spring, with the remainder of the summer being very hot and dry. With low humidity the summer temperatures often exceed 100 degrees Fahrenheit.

Topography varies from prairie country to mountain ground; most of the ranch's soils are a mountain loam while some areas have a lot of small stones. The B Bar M Ranch lies in the very centre of Montana in the Judith Basin surrounded by five mountain ranges, Big Snowies, Little Snowies, Judiths, Little Belts and the Highwood mountains.

The Pester's ranch comprises 1,800 deeded (freehold) acres and 3,200 leased acres. The B Bar M Ranch has 4,400 tillable acres in rotation with alfalfa and grass hay,

hard red winter wheat, hard red spring wheat, and barley. 600 acres of the ranch is in native pasture for the raising of Black Angus cattle.

"We normally get one cutting of hay a year using any re-growth for fall and winter pasture. The hay yields between 1 and 2½ tons/acre depending on precipitation. We put hay up in 1,500lb round bales. We sell surplus hay as stock cow hay," says Bruce.

The Pester's run a cow-calf operation with Black Angus cows bred to Black Angus bulls. Cows are calved out in February and March, normally weaning a 700lb calf in late October. Steer calves go to feeders (feedlots) in the Midwestern United States where they are finished. The heifer calves are grown on at the ranch and marketed as replacement females.

Through the winter months the cattle are fed a ground ration of wheat straw and alfalfa hay. It takes about two and a half tons of feed to winter a cow in this area. The number of cow calf pairs Bruce and Melinda run on the ranch varies from 100-200 pairs depending on rainfall, prices and rotations.

Water for the cattle is supplied by pipeline from a 1,325ft deep artesian well; reservoirs are also used that are filled by melting snow in the spring.

The arable land is usually all in crop, as the Pesters don't normally summer fallow their land unless in a drought situation, where as farmers further north follow the typical prairie summer fallow practice.

Hard red winter wheat is the main cash grain crop, grain crops are seeded at 60lb/acre. Second winter wheat crop yields about 40 bushels per acre, (a bushel is 60 pounds) with summer fallow winter wheat yields between 60 to 80 bushels per acre.

Spring wheat and barley yield between 25 to 40 bushels per acre; the spring crops are

The farm comprises 4,400 acres of wheat and barley, with 600 acres of hilly ground as natural pasture.

secondary crops, as they are not really suited to the mid-Montana rainfall patterns.

The hard red wheats are exported off the west coast to Japan and other Pacific Rim countries. All straw from the grain crops is baled for winter feed needs.

Bruce Pester says, "Our farming practices over the last 15 years have changed considerably from relying on tillage to now, no-till, also called direct seeding. This has resulted in a dramatic shift away from the horsepower and man-hours once needed to produce a grain crop. Melinda and I do most of the labour and management ourselves, we take on three part-time employees during haying and grain harvest. Nowadays, more time is spent on a combine than on a tractor."

Bruce explained how his interest in JD Wagner tractors came about: "When I was a kid on my dad's farm, I couldn't wait to drive a tractor, so dad put me on a gas Case LA tractor pulling a 12ft one-way disc plough. Dad soon realised this tractor was much too thirsty for fuel so in 1974 he bought a used JD WA-14 as a second tractor for me to run.

"This tractor proved to be a real workhorse able, to mouldboard plough 80 acres a day 12 inches deep, or summer fallow 300 acres a day. When I got started farming on my own, I bought the tractor from Dad, and I still use it today.

"These Wagner tractors weigh between 30,000 and 32,000lb (14.28 tons) with ballast. This makes for a very sure-footed tractor with an excellent ride. Newer tractors today

Bruce Pester praises his John Deere WA-14.

weigh much less per horsepower, resulting in power hop and a much rougher ride.

"We also own a 956 Versatile 335hp tractor weighing in at 25,000lb. After a 20-minute ride you feel like you got bucked off, once power hop starts the ride becomes so uncomfortable you have to stop the tractor and start again."

Bruce relies on these thirty-year-old tractors for most of his farming operation, saying they are reliable, easy to work on and easy to maintain. His philosophy of 'why change if it works well' shows.

"Even though these tractors are very basic, they are comfy and good to drive. The power from the dependable Cummins engine and the reliable Fuller Roadranger transmission allows me to pull a 40ft Flexi Coil 5000 air seeder at around 4.8mph. In a 15-hour day I can plant in the region of 300 acres of wheat.

"My John Deere Wagners are cheap, efficient horsepower, so why change to a quarter-of-a-million dollar modern four-wheel drive articulated tractor full of unnecessary electronic gadgets, there just aren't the returns in farming today."

Bruce's interest in JD Wagners peeked around three years ago when a tractor collector drove in the yard and wanted to buy his JD WA-14 number one.

"I did not know at that time it was the first WA-14 built for JD. I always thought it odd that a Wagner should be painted John Deere green, it always seemed like JD didn't claim these tractors.

"Wanting to do some research, I was unable to find any information on the internet or from the John Deere archives. I finally found an article about them in the *Ultimate Tractor Power: Volume 2* book.

"I later contacted Dave Curtis, a former Wagner dealer, who verified this tractor was the first JD WA-14. I have since added to my John Deere Wagner line up with a further JD WA-14 and a JD WA-17. The JD WA-14 number one will always be my favourite tractor for work, it will be my project restoring and showing this tractor when I retire." ∎

Serial number WA-14 000111 was Bruce's third JD Wagner, seen fitted with an 11-cubic yard scraper box for land-levelling duties.

The sole survivor?

While in the USA, Peter D Simpson was surprised by a tractor that he'd never seen, or even heard of, before… a Kirschmann.

After compiling the A-Z of articulated tractors around the world in the *Ultimate Tractor Power* series of books, which includes virtually every production four-wheel drive articulated tractor built, one or two makes were bound to have slipped through the net.

With this in mind I made it my personal crusade to try and track down every production articulated tractor ever built, along with the manufacturers where possible.

While filming with Bernhard Roes and DT-Media for the *Big Iron* series of videos during May 2004, we were on a farm in New York State looking at an old Minneapolis-Moline A4T-1600 that was too far gone for filming,

when the owner of this tractor said he had something special to show us.

He didn't tell me it was a four-wheel drive or a limited production run tractor, but there it was, a Kirschmann – a name I had never come across before.

It started its life as a prototype intended to become a production tractor, despite the production run being only for a very short period during 1970/71.

Weighing in at around 11 tons, the heavy-duty tractor had a constantly-variable hydrostatic transmission.

Left: The Caterpillar six-cylinder 1673 Series C engine producing in the region of 300hp.

Below: A simple back end consisted of a swinging drawbar and a couple of hydraulic couplings.

auction in 2003 at Prairie City, South Dakota, for $8,000 (approx. £4,200).

The tractor in question had spent its working life on a Midwest corn farm working on flat land. It weighs in at around 11 tons and has an estimated 300hp. It will probably never work on the farm but it certainly looks ready for the grunt and heave of heavy work.

Built by John Kirschmann in 1970/71, the tractor was one of only three built. It is believed that the other two tractors have been scrapped. It was fully intended for the Kirschmann to become a production tractor, as at that time farming across the US was at an all-time high and returns for those that worked the land were good.

Labour was reducing on the farm as many young available workers were heading into the big towns and cities for more lucrative work; the early 1970s was a great time for high horsepower tractor production and big equipment development.

If Kirschmann's plans for tractor production had progressed, who knows where he would have been today in the tractor manufacturing world. Kirschmann designed and built many other agricultural products including the Willmar self-propelled sprayer, which was being developed at the same time as the tractor. The decision was made to continue with developing sprayers, as the demand was ➡

Key facts

Built:	USA
Engine:	6-cyl Caterpillar 1673 Series C
Power:	300hp
Chassis:	Articulated, four-wheel drive
Typical farm:	Large American arable

John Voepel's farm in Newfane, Niagara, New York State is 5,000 acres of mainly cabbages and corn; he requires reasonably light and manoeuvrable tractors for row crop work, but with enough power and traction for all the ploughing and heavy tillage operations.

The Minneapolis-Moline proved ideal and used to do all the heavy work. Due to its age it was retired several years back, as the new breed of rigid-framed 'front-wheel assist' tractors, as they call them in the States, fit the bill nicely – yet John says the lighter articulated four-wheel drives are still the most suitable for his operation.

John has been a keen collector of the big four-wheel drives for a number of years and came across the rare Kirschmann at an

The operator's cab on this prototype was very basic.

greater at that time and he ceased tractor development as there were many other tractor producers out there. Kirschmann felt competition was too intense. Eventually Willmar sprayers was bought out by AGCO.

The key phrase during the early 1970s amongst farmers across America was 'Traction, Flotation and Compaction'. Farmers were becoming more conscious of soil structure damage and the resulting crop yield loss.

Traction was extremely good and despite the heavyweight construction of the tractor, it is estimated that the Kirschmann only put down about 10lb/psi; capable of floating

across the light dry land. Causing minimal compaction damage in the wet season, this tractor proved its worth in field tests during the fall (autumn) of 1970.

The tractor was designed and built following a standard articulating design with four equal-sized wheels which were shod with 23.1-30 8-ply Silverstone tyres all round.

The engine and operator cabin were on the front unit with 40 degrees of articulation and 15 degrees of oscillation from the centre line. The rear unit was simple, a rear axle with swinging drawbar and hydraulic couplings.

The dependable in-line six-cylinder CAT 1673 Series C engine, rated at around 300hp, powers the tractor while the transmission is a hydraulic drive direct from the engine, which gives a constantly-variable hydrostatic transmission.

The operator cab on this prototype is very basic, but high and wide enough for the operator to stand up and stretch when working long hours at a time, and the operator's seat swivelled.

Full air conditioning was a must, but there were very few other refinements. Instrumentation was limited – even the rev counter was mounted on the bonnet outside the cab. The controls; a throttle, brake pedal and forward/reverse lever are all that feature.

The downside would have been that the cab was extremely noisy and must have vibrated tremendously, as it was all steel with no padding to muffle the noise.

No doubt, if the tractor had gone into full production the cab and operator needs would have been given higher priority. ∎

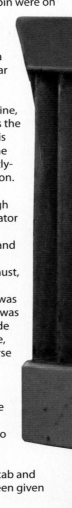

Like most other things on the tractor, the pivot point was simple, yet did the job.

When working, the tractor would have been equipped with 23.1-30 8-ply duals all round.

Wrexham revelation

A rare model in its home country, an immaculate Minneapolis-Moline A4T in North Wales is probably unique. Peter D Simpson went to investigate.

The four-wheel drive Minneapolis-Moline A4T-1600 was built in Charles City, Iowa and it towered over its yellow two-wheel drive cousins.

Occasionally, a surviving model can be found still hard at work on a small farm in America's Mid-West. So just what is an A4T? And why is this tractor thousands of miles away from its former home?

Brief history

As the trend for more power on the farm continued throughout the 1960s, it became clear to Minneapolis-Moline engineers that there was only one way forward to make effective use of higher horsepower.

This was the production of a four-wheel drive tractor to achieve the correct power-to-weight ratio. In common with other leading manufacturers, Minneapolis-Moline factory projections indicated a need for a 200hp tractor by the year 1975.

Sadly, M-M never reached this target, as big tractor production ceased in early 1972 when its parent company, White Motor Corporation, restructured its farm equipment operation.

In 1958, Minneapolis-Moline dealer Don Oliver built his own four-wheel drive articulated tractor from off-the-shelf M-M components.

Ten years later, M-M President Don Cox visited Don Oliver at his home in Stuttgart, Arkansas. Together they studied the

Roy Bailey's immaculate M-M A4T-1600 arrived in the UK in the autumn of 2003.

MINNEAPOLIS·MOLINE

A4T-1600

New components for the tractor included a front and rear frame, an articulation joint and driveline system, new operator cab, modified tin work, fuel tanks, extra plumbing and wiring for the electronics. The later units included a three-point hitch and pto.

The A4T-1600 was also produced as the green Oliver 2655 with total production of 244 Olivers and 1,043 A4T-1600s built between 1970 and 1972. Several tractors were badged as the deep red, White Plainsman A4T-1600 diesel, these were produced in 1970.

Minneapolis-Moline in Wales

Classic Minneapolis-Moline and Oliver enthusiast Ray Bailey has been a dedicated collector of Minneapolis-Moline tractor for a number of years.

On one of his trips to America to visit fellow M-M enthusiasts, Ray came across an old A4T-1600 and instantly made the decision to purchase it.

That was in 1998, but it was not until autumn 2003 the tractor headed from America to Southampton docks then travelled north to Wrexham. This Goliath machine definitely made heads turn when it paraded alongside many smaller M-Ms and Oliver tractors at its first outing at the Mid-Shropshire Vintage Show the following year.

Ray used to work as a mechanic for an International Harvester dealership in Oswestry in the 1950s. His interest in collecting tractors started while working at this dealership. His overall interest was in both American and UK-built IH tractors and their derivatives. The W-9 was always a great favourite with Ray. ➡

workshop-built tractor and Cox decided the company could build a tractor similar to that created by Oliver.

Key facts

Built:	Minnesota, USA
Engine:	6-cyl Minneapolis-Moline D585
Power:	169hp
Chassis:	Articulated, four-wheel drive
Typical farm:	American arable

The M-M company's main problem was the projected low production numbers of a four-wheel drive tractor. It dictated the decision by M-M to use as many components as possible from models of tractors already in production. Designing a component-built machine kept build costs to a minimum, as well as speeding up development time.

The first tractor was an engineering feat. The original plan commenced with a rough sketch in March 1969. This was transformed into a running prototype by May of the same year. A production tractor was ready by the November of 1969. This was an impressive testimony to the Moline company's engineering skills.

The first prototype model of the Minneapolis Moline A4T-1400 was painted in the familiar M-M yellow livery. By the time the tractor became a full production model it was finished in a new, deep red/orange colour, although decals and other finish details remained the same as previous M-M tractors.

The first production tractors were an A4T-1400 diesel and the LPG-powered A4T-1600 in 1969, followed by the diesel-powered A4T-1600 in 1970. That first production A4T-1400 used the same M-M D504A-6 six-cylinder diesel engine as the G-1050 two-wheel drive tractor; a turbo kit was produced for the A4T-1400 lifting its power to 139hp at 1,800rpm.

With the release of the diesel A4T-1600, the same six-cylinder engine was sourced from the two-wheel drive G-1355.

The transmission unit was the same as the one in the G-1350 tractor, a two-speed manual-shift drop box (transfer case) was added behind the transmission.

The drive axles were the same as on the two-wheel drive G-950 with the brake units from the G-1350. Other common components included hydraulics, radiators, wheels, hubs, instrumentation and seat.

The pivot point of the A4T-1600, which has 44° of articulation, compared to many similar tractors offering only 40°.

Technical specification

Produced:	1970-1972
Engine:	Minneapolis-Moline D585
Cylinders:	6
Displacement:	585cu in
Engine horsepower:	169hp
PTO horsepower:	143hp
Transmission:	10 forward, 2 reverse
Top speed:	22.2mph
Linkage:	Three-point and swinging drawbar
Fuel capacity:	83½ gallons
Wheelbase:	120in
Width:	96in (minimum)
Height:	116in (to top of exhaust)
Turning circle:	15.6ft (to centre line)
Weight:	7.72 tonnes
Tyre sizes:	18.4x38 8-ply

A driver's eye view of the instrument panel.

While searching for a W-9 for his collection he came across Tony Weaver, who had farmed with M-M tractors during the war and who had an M-M UTS for sale. After a last unsuccessful attempt to find a W-9, he went back to Tony and came away with the 1941 UTS, rated at 37.23hp at the belt.

Over the following years Ray acquired several M-Ms on farms around the UK and once back home he undertook full restorations.

Ray became an avid enthusiast for the yellow Minneapolis-Moline tractors. From 1977 through to the late 1980s he continued

The A4T-1600 was built utilising many parts that were used on production two-wheel drive M-M and Oliver tractors.

A three-point linkage with draft sensing, 20gpm closed-centre hydraulics and 1,000rpm pto made the tractor suitable for most farming applications.

buying and restoring them and expanding his collection to include a rare UDM, as well as UDS, 4 Star Diesel, UB Special, UTI ZB, UNI-Harvester plus many other models.

During 1991, Ray visited North America for the first time. "I had restored and collected American tractors for a number of years, now I wanted to see them in their homeland of Iowa and Minnesota."

"During my three-week visit I met some great people, the farmers I encountered were most hospitable and I learnt so much about the yellow Minneapolis tractors.

"While in Western Iowa I had the chance to visit the late Roger Mohr's museum, which contained over 70 Minneapolis-Moline tractors, to my delight and amazement Roger still farmed with several Minneapolis-Moline tractors.

"While I was visiting Roger, Tiny Blom, a keen Oliver tractor collector arrived. He invited me back to see his private collection of more than 70 Olivers."

This chance meeting with Tiny Blom led to a lasting friendship, each year Ray would fly back to Iowa to spend time with his newfound friends. "On one visit, Tiny and I discussed the ins and outs of collecting tractors and how a collection should be managed, I think it was at this point that I decided I was going to specialise in the rare and unusual American tractors of the Minneapolis-Moline family and their derivatives."

While on a visit to Iowa in 1997 Ray found a big Moline in a hedge bottom. It was a sad-looking M-M A4T-1600 four-wheel drive tractor, which had been robbed for various spare parts. As he looked at it, Ray thought: 'this is definitely a rare machine, which would look good in my collection'.

Ray added: "The tyres were totally worn out, the engine was seized on number-two cylinder and the big ends were shot.

"After a while decision-making and a few phone calls later, I decided to offer its

owner a price that we were both happy with and the tractor was mine. Even after the purchase I was still unsure whether what I had just done was the right decision, but a rare M-M tractor was what I was looking for and this was ideal."

Through his new found friends it was decided to repair and restore the tractor in Iowa; one friend completely stripped and rebuilt the engine over a two-year period, while another friend undertook all the body and paint work. In all, it took four years of part time work for the A4T to be fully restored to its former glory. ■

Production details

Year	Serial number	No. built
1970	45600001-45600187	186
1971	45600188-45600700	612
1972	45600701-45601190	489

British powerhouse

Peter D Simpson looks in depth at a slice of UK history, the MF 1200.

Massey Ferguson in America was a key player in the four-wheel drive articulated tractor market, holding a strong position for more than 20 years. It all started in 1971 with the introduction of the MF 1500 and 1800.

During the 1960s, Wagner, Steiger, Versatile, IH, John Deere and Case were the main four-wheel drive manufacturers and by the end of that decade four-wheel drives were being accepted by farmers from coast to coast, who were looking for more tillage power from the leading companies.

This was a growing market that Massey Ferguson was missing out on and so, in 1971, two new four-wheel drive models hit the American market: the MF 1500 at 150hp and the MF 1800 at 180hp.

The first MF four-wheel drives gave the company a new horsepower range that competed successfully with the opposition. The Massey and Massey Ferguson names were strong across America and Canada and the new tractors quickly gained acceptance,

The Massey Ferguson 1200 is a true icon of British agriculture.

Key facts

Built:	Manchester, UK
Engine:	6-cyl Perkins A6.354
Power:	105hp
Chassis:	Articulated, four-wheel drive
Typical farm:	Large European arable

The Massey Ferguson is ideally suited to both drawbar and three-point linkage work as weight is spread 50:50 when under load.

eating into the competition's stranglehold during the early 1970s.

Such was the success of these tractors in America that Massey Ferguson management decided a British equivalent should be produced for both the home and European markets and so the 105hp MF 1200 was introduced in 1972. These were built at the Barton Dock Road plant with a few constructed at the nearby Central Parts Operation.

The release of the MF 1200 four-wheel drive was the first time most UK farmers and tractor drivers had seen such a machine. A few had seen the big American prairie-busters like the 1969 Series I Steigers or the early Versatile D-118, 125 and 145 of the late 1960s in the farming press, but never in real life.

The new MF 1200 was to take the big farms at home by storm. The progressive farmer could see the way forward and

mechanise his farm with greater work rates, maximising profitability. Here was a chance to use bigger, more efficient implements on the farm yet run an economical tractor.

The power of the MF 1200 may not have been as great as on some of Ernest Doe's Triple 'D' tractors or the American imported two-wheel drive machines, but here we ➡

The six-cylinder Perkins A6.354 powered the Massey Ferguson 1200, producing 105hp (DIN).

A sales brochure for the MF 1200 tractor.

Specifications

Model	MF 1200	MF 1250
Engine	Perkins A6.354	Perkins A6.354.4
Power	105hp (DIN)	112hp (DIN)
PTO power	91.2hp	96hp
Cylinders	6	6 (turbo optional)
Displacement	354cu in	
Fuel capacity	70 gallons (318 litres)	
Transmission	12 forward, 4 reverse Multi-Power	12 forward, 4 reverse Multi-Power MkII
Turning radius	12ft 2in (3,720mm)	
Length	203.5in (5,170mm)	
Wheelbase	100.75in (2,560mm)	
Height	116in (2,950mm) to top of cab	
Weight	5,156kg	6,203kg
Tyre size	12x38 or 15x30	

Above right: MF 1200 front grille (top) and MF 1250 front grille (lower).

had a British-built tractor with even weight distribution over four driven equal-sized wheels using the power more effortlessly and more efficiently.

The MF 1200 had remarkable traction and manoeuvrability, especially in adverse conditions. The tractor was not over-heavy – weighing in at a little over five tons, and it was a very versatile workhorse, capable of many operations from heavy tillage to top work. With its top road speed of 17.45 mph it was also a useful and safe machine for road haulage work.

MF introduced unparalleled standards of power and comfort to the 100-plus horsepower market with the 1200. It was the first four-wheel drive to be built in Britain by Massey Ferguson and the first to offer the most complete ready-for-the-field four-wheel drive specification available.

The articulated tractor, by way of its design, offered maximum traction and manoeuvrability. The Perkins six-cylinder engine and operator cab were mounted on the forward chassis with the hydraulics, three-point linkage and pto built into the rear unit.

Designed from the outset as a true four-wheel drive tractor with four equal-sized wheels, the Massey Ferguson 1200 avoided many of the inherent disadvantages of its more conventional four-wheel drive competitors that were simply conversions of existing two-wheel-drive tractors.

The weight distribution gave a loading of 68 per cent on the front axle and, when a mounted implement was put into work, weight was transferred 50:50 between front and rear axles, producing maximum traction at each wheel.

Left: The articulated, four-wheel drive MF 1200 enjoyed an eight-year production run before being updated to the MF 1250 in 1980.

Articulating 42° in either direction, the 1200 and 1250 models have a minimum turning radius of 12ft 2in.

The two units were hinged so that they could turn 42° left or right and the rear unit could pivot independently of the front unit 15° of centre line in either direction, allowing the wheels to follow the most difficult ground contours. The 1200's turning radius was 12 feet 2 inches, ideal for headland turns.

The 1200 was powered by a Perkins A6.354 six-cylinder diesel engine rated at 105hp (DIN) at 2,400rpm with an independent 1,000rpm pto rated at 87hp at 2,216rpm. The transmission was an MF Multi-Power unit with 12 forward and four reverse speeds.

The MF 1200 enjoyed an eight-year production run before being updated to the MF 1250 in 1980. This was basically identical to the 1200, using the same frames, cabin, and tin work, but several slight cosmetic changes included a different front grille and decals. The new 112hp tractor was produced until 1982.

Ironing out the few minor faults of the successful 1200, the 1250 was powered by a new six-cylinder Perkins A6.354.4 diesel engine rated at 112hp at 2,400rpm. A dealer-fitted turbocharger was offered as an option. Still using an independent 1,000rpm pto rated at 96hp at 2,216rpm, the 1250 was

being left behind by other manufacturers who were beginning to produce higher horsepower, rigid frame, front-wheel assist tractors.

The improved Hydrostatic steering ensured the 1250 was light to steer with positive control at all engine speeds by ➡

Massey Ferguson's first articulated models

Model	Country built	Produced	Power
MF 1500	United States of America	1971-75	150hp
MF 1800	United States of America	1971-75	180hp
MF 1200	United Kingdom	1972-80	105hp
MF 1505	United States of America	1975-77	174hp
MF 1805	United States of America	1975-77	192hp
MF 1250	United Kingdom	1980-82	112hp

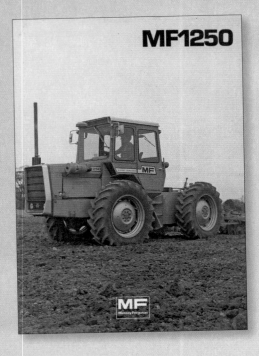

MF1250

Left: A sales brochure for the MF 1250 tractor.

way of a simplified and completely independent hydraulic circuit which had its own reservoir, pump and filtration system.

Other changes included the Mark II Multi-Power transmission and heavy-duty clutch. The 12-speed transmission provided the facility of increasing either ground speed or torque by the flick of a switch without stopping or declutching.

The rear axle was strengthened as was the category II three-point linkage, which had a 28 per cent increased lift capacity to 9,625lb (4,375kg).

A larger lift assistor ram was fitted and the entire linkage was either redesigned or strengthened. Along with many other small changes and modifications, the 1250 gave improved running, operation and maintenance for greater efficiency and reliability.

By 1982, Massey Ferguson four-wheel drive tractor production finished in the UK and the more powerful American-built four-wheel drives were imported into the UK in smaller numbers.

With the introduction of the MF 4000 range in 1978 the four-wheel drive market took on new boundaries with horsepower exceeding the 300hp mark.

The MF 1200 and 1250 are a pair of true British classics that are rarely seen at work today. One or other of these two greats might be found working in the timber industry or occasionally working on a farm but recently these tractors have been turning up at auction with the majority of models heading for preservation.

Rated at 105 and 112 DIN horsepower respectively, these articulated tractors were big machines in their day. With tremendous traction and pulling power they were ideally suited for heavy cultivation work in the UK.

It was not long before they were superseded in the race for higher horsepower – the front-wheel assist or conventional four-wheel drive tractors, as we know them, soon exceeded the MF 1250's power and performance – and so the UK's only true four-wheel drive articulated tractors ceased production and joined many other British greats in the history books. ∎

Right: Instrumentation in the MF 1200 was similar to other Massey Ferguson models of the period. The familiar tractormeter and associated analogue dials, along with the Multi-Power controller, made drivers of smaller MFs feel immediately at home.

Below: The rear axle was strengthened on the Massey Ferguson 1250, as was the category II three-point linkage. Lift capacity was increased by 28 per cent to a substantial 9,625lb (4,375kg), perfect for even the heaviest of implements.

Dual wheels are the key to many of the Muir-Hills in East Sussex.

Resting in peace

Muir-Hills are not common but they're still out there, Kim Parks discovers.

East Sussex and Kent have always been prolific areas for Muir-Hill tractors, particularly from the 1970s until the 1990s when local Ford dealer Sussex Tractors, of Uckfield, was also agent for this marque.

Owners who had tried the tractors once, then added to their fleets by buying second-hand, but Muir-Hills have now become a disappearing breed. However, I tracked down no less than seven examples in the area and they were just about intact.

The Muir-Hill has been an ideal tractor for arable farmers and was an attractive alternative, particularly price-wise, when compared to a new Roadless or County. One big advantage was its turning circle – a major benefit in this part of the world, where it is quite hilly and farmers are working in small fields.

Arable farming

Staplecross Farm falls into this landscape and belongs to John and Tim Lister, a father-and-son combination who have farmed there for many years, catering for livestock and crops.

Now concentrating on arable farming, they do not contract anything out except the combining on the 400-acre farm. Even with such a large acreage it struggles to break even and so they supplement their income by running dog kennels.

Key facts

Built:	Gloucestershire , UK
Engine:	6-cyl Ford 2715E
Power:	120hp
Chassis:	Rigid, four-wheel drive
Typical farm:	Large British arable

Another of the farm's Muir-Hills was a 1976 121A, KVG 739P, which the family purchased second-hand in 1984 from Robert Wraight, of Ashford, Kent, the well-known export tractor dealer.

A good many of this breed worked in east Kent on large vegetable farms, which are relatively flat and near the English Channel and this example is interesting because it features a DAF 8.25-litre 180-200hp straight six-cylinder engine that came from a dump truck and was converted before it arrived here in the 1980s.

The bonnet was lengthened by 300mm and this hybrid featured super single wheels and was used for light cultivation. "She doesn't carry a clock, but is a real 'goer'", I was told.

Staplecross Farm had more Muir-Hills that were basically in retirement, including a 101 that was in the brambles going green a few years ago! However, Tim had brought it into the farmyard, power-washed it and planned to restore it.

It was fitted with the standard factory cab, but was door-less. The Ford engine ran a treat; the brakes were holding up well and at least it was in the dry and not rotting away. The tractor showed 2,600 hours but again it had gone round the clock! It was originally supplied by Sussex Tractors, but arrived on the farm second-hand in 1978.

The fleet was completed by another 121, this time a Series II 1973 model with 6,856 hours on the clock. It sat in the barn with the 101 and eventually is to be returned to its former glory. It ran well and was bought second-hand in 1981.

Above: Muir-Hill 121 Series III decals.

Below: This Muir-Hill 121 features super single tyres and is powered by a DAF 8.25-litre engine.

The Lister family had nothing but good to say about the Muir-Hill experience, but time caught up with them in 1990 when the farm changed from mixed to arable and they wanted even more horsepower.

Mixed farming

The next three Muir-Hills I went to see all had flat batteries, so I couldn't run them up – they really were resting! They were at Crowhurst near West St Leonards, Hastings, on a 300-acre arable and grassland farm and included a 1976 121 Series II, LPX 25R, fitted with a Ford 2715E engine and Ford Dual Power transmission, that was introduced during the later period of production of this model. ➡

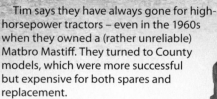

Tim says they have always gone for high-horsepower tractors – even in the 1960s when they owned a (rather unreliable) Matbro Mastiff. They turned to County models, which were more successful but expensive for both spares and replacement.

So they looked for an alternative and the first Muir-Hill to arrive came new in 1976. It was a 121A, NPN 646P, fitted with the Ford 2715E six-cylinder engine and standard Ford gearbox. It proved a good tractor and the clock read 5,331 hours on my visit, but it had already been round once!

It was used for light cultivation and drilling and, at the time of the picture here, was attached to a Simba tool carrier with a Parmiter zig-zag harrow on it.

Bill Vernon's Muir-Hill 121 is used with a Bomford Supertrim hedgecutter in the winter months.

The hour meter was broken, but it was very much a standard tractor. On the rear end was a Bomford Supertrim hedgecutter – the tractor spending the winter months tidying hedges. In the past, the winter weather had been serious here and a front snow plough attachment bracket came in very handy.

The best of the lot was a 121 Series III, a type introduced by Muir-Hill in 1978. This 1979 example, BVC 413T, featured the

A sales brochure for the Muir-Hill 121 tractor.

Spacecab, which is wider and better sound-proofed than its predecessor, has the air conditioning unit on the roof and only one door.

The tractor featured a turbocharged Ford 2704E 143hp engine, which was standard on the 141 models. It was regularly used on the farm with its Dual Power Ford 16x4 transmission.

The hours on the tractor showed 2,311, but as much of the arable work on the farm was carried out by contractors, it was unlikely to accumulate too many more.

Sitting on its dual wheels it certainly looked a handsome beast, but the tyres restricted its turning circle. That was compounded by the fact that all three of the Muir-Hills I saw that day (fitted with dual wheels and super singles) had their cab steps removed. One got the feeling you would have to be very athletic and fit simply to get in them.

The tractor came from Holt Tractors, of Hailsham, East Sussex, had been a very reliable machine and worked with a power harrow for many years.

Owner Bill Vernon then displayed a 1980 Muir-Hill 141. This example was fitted with the Ford 2704E turbocharged 143hp engine, Dual Power transmission and the Spacecab. It had completed 3,470 hours, which I felt was genuine.

This 1980 example came from East Anglia, worked occasionally and was going a little rusty around the edges. It represented the period when Muir-Hill was starting to hit hard times, which culminated in its owner, Babcock International, stopping production in October 1982. ■

This Muir-Hill 121 Series III was a clean tractor and possibly the best one I was to see on the day.

Runaway rarity

Howard Sherren discovers how a family saved a tractor from the scrapyard after a horrific accident.

The Charnley family are renowned for their passion for Nuffield, Leyland and Marshall tractors but have recently turned their attention to the derivatives.

They enjoy nothing more than restoring machines to impeccable condition, often when there is limited work over the winter months for the family firm of John Charnley & Sons, which is run by Will and David Charnley.

This year saw the completion of their latest project, a rare Bray Four 70, which arrived with on a pallet!

The story starts some 10 years ago when Will and David found out about this rather rare unit, which was in a rather sorry state.

The Bray Four 70 was supplied new on 28 February 1973, to mining company Lye & Co, which was based in the small town of Bridge of Earn, near Perth in Scotland.

This particular Four 70 (registration WES 537L) came fitted with an astonishing front blade and was possibly used to aid the extraction of coal. As with many mining and industrial tractors, it received a very tough time and was worked hard.

Years of abuse took their toll with lots of welding of cracks, rot and possibly a lot of wear to the handbrake considering what happened at the end of its working life – it somehow managed to career out of control down a hill at the mine, which lead to both stub axles being snapped cleanly off.

Key facts

Built:	Gloucestershire, UK
Engine:	4-cyl Leyland 4/98 NT
Power:	72hp
Chassis:	Rigid, four-wheel drive
Typical farm:	Large British arable

The Bray Four 70 is a rare beast, this one is of two to exist from around 40 built.

Technical specification

Produced:	1973-1975
Engine:	Leyland 4/98 NT
Engine power:	72hp
PTO power:	65hp
Cylinders:	4
Bore x stroke:	98mm x 125mm
Displacement:	3,770cc
Fuel capacity:	68 litres
Top speed:	19.66mph
Transmission:	10 forward, 2 reverse
Turning circle:	11,890mm
Length:	4,060mm
Width:	2,000mm
Weight:	3,741kg
Cab:	Leyalnd safety
Tyre sizes:	12x36
Price new (1975):	£6,725

Above: The Bray Four 70 when it arrived in the Charnley's yard. Photo: The Charnley family.

Left: The teeth on the front axle drive gears had been stripped. Photo: The Charnley family.

After this horrendous accident the tractor was parked up and used as a donor tractor for the other Leyland tractors being used there.

Stripped of most of its parts, the skid unit was sold to collector Paul Wilson and remained in his hands until the Charnleys persuaded him to part with it in 2004 and contemplated the mammoth job of reconstructing this unique machine.

When the Four 70 arrived at the Charnleys' yard (on a pallet) it was in a very bad way – for a start, most projects at least come with wheels!

The skid unit had no engine, hydraulic top cover, cab or mudguards and had been robbed of most useful parts. But this wasn't a problem for the family, who had plentiful supplies of new and used spares for Leyland tractors as part of their business; the biggest headache was when the transmission was checked out.

Will explained: "We had a shock when we lifted the transmission cover off. Not only had the accident stripped the teeth off the four front axle drive gears, it had also bent the pinion shaft."

It was found that the gears were specifically cut for Bray and were only supplied to that company, which meant sourcing them was going to be a nightmare. Lots of gear suppliers were contacted with part numbers and the search began for replacements.

The pinion shaft was luckily a Leyland part and easily sourced, but the gears drew a blank.

The only option left was to have the gears cut to the exact specification at a whopping cost of £2,000, the biggest single expense to the whole restoration.

"On the plus side we do now have a spare set in stock if they are ever required in the future," laughed Will.

With the gearbox sorted, the Charnleys turned their attention to finding the rest of the missing parts such as the engine, cab and wheels.

The engine came from a Bray 384 which had been fitted with a rebuilt 4/98 NT engine which badly vibrated. It was found that the balancing weights had not been ➡

History

In March 1971, Bray Construction Equipment sold its manufacturing site and moved to a new ten-acre site at Tetbury, Gloucestershire, where it continued building four-wheel drive machines.

The Bray Four 70 was basically an updated version of its Four 384 model and a continued answer to farmers wanting more power, traction and stability.

The Four 384 was the first Bray to be based on the new design and colour of British Leyland tractors revealed at the 1969 Smithfield Show.

This particular model was built until 1972 when Leyland changed its engines and model designation. Instead of engine capacity and cylinders, the new Leyland models became the number of driven wheels and engine power. With the 384 becoming the 270, the Bray was also updated to the Four 70 in 1973.

It used the same 4/98 NT diesel engine with a CAV rotary pump and the same back end and safety cab as the 270.

Priced at £6,725 in 1975, the newer model was considerably more expensive than the previous model, which had been just half this figure.

Bray was sold to Matbro in November 1973 which, along with the introduction of Q cabs, lead to production ceasing in 1976 along with that of some of the competition.

At the time there were three major rivals – County, Roadless and Muir-Hill, although all these equal-wheel machines were losing market share to unequal-wheeled units thanks to their reduced price and better manoeuvrability.

The most similar machine would have been the Leyland 4100, which used County parts to produce an equal-wheel unit and, along with the 485, ceased production in 1976 due to costs involved in adapting a Q cab to meet government regulations and the decline in sales.

This resulted in no more than 40 Four 70 models being produced; it is believed many were exported to South America but now only two are known to have survived – the model featured here and another in Sweden.

A heavy-duty Jefferson linkage was added to the tractor to improve the specification.

Statistics

The four-cylinder Leyland 4/98 NT engine had a 3.8 litre capacity and gave 78.6Nm of torque at 1,300rpm.

The stroke was long at 125mm and the bore was 98mm, which was actually less than the previous ex-BMC unit used in the Nuffield-based models. This was to improve reliability and weaknesses found with the 100mm design.

The engine transmitted its power through a 12-forward and 2-reverse gearbox, which had eight normal gears, with two high speeds designated for road work. This gave speeds from 1.61mph, right through to 19.66mph, which wasn't bad considering the power and the weight of the tractor.

Hydraulics came courtesy of a gear pump offering 30.2 litres a minute at 2,250rpm, which resulted in an 1,814kg lift capacity or 2,721kg lift with the additional assistor ram.

Stopping power was down to disc-type brakes that were of the self-energising variety, which also helped to get the turning circle down to 7.93m from a massive 11.89m.

The Bray's front axle was primarily the same as the company used on its loading shovels – a sphere-type stub axle and the same steering joints, along with the same planetary hub reduction gears.

The front axle drive was driven by a drop box fitted to the existing Leyland gearbox through a spur gear and a propeller shaft, and it also featured a front differential lock.

This idea worked better than the County version when it came to steering lock as there were no shafts to get in the way of the front wheels, improving the angle.

Cover plates were fitted to the underneath of the front axle, up to the rear in the form of an A, which protected the drive shaft and sump from possible damage when carrying out forestry work.

The Four 70 had six-ply, 12x36 tyres fitted as standard with optional 12x38, 14x30 and 15x30 available on request to suit every operation.

The machine's statistics were rather impressive. With a weight of 3,741kg, 4,060mm length and 2,000mm width, its presence was imposing.

fitted previously, so these were included and the engine ran a treat.

The front axle castings were obtained from an old loading shovel and required re-chroming, new seals and bearings before being fitted to the chassis.

The front wheels actually came separately with the tractor so they were cleaned down and re-sprayed, along with a pair of Power Adjustable Variable Track (PAVT) adjustable rims at the back.

All the rims were treated to a set of very striking 18.4 R30 Goodyear Super Traction

radials while the brakes were overhauled with new discs and expanders.

A Leyland 270 donated a hydraulic top cover, along with footplates, mudguards and cab.

Will said: "We wanted the tractor to be a full-specification machine and tried to fit every extra possible."

So, a heavy-duty Jefferson linkage was located – these were available on Leyland tractors at the time of manufacture – to make the tractor look a little more purposeful.

A pick-up hitch and 13 Leyland front weights, giving 429kg extra ballast, were found and added before everything was given several coats of red oxide and finished in Leyland light and dark blue synthetic paint.

With many of the parts off the shelf, the finished product is nothing but outstanding and the two years work definitely worth their while.

The tractor has already visited a number of shows this year and has stunned crowds, largely because of its history.

Above: Fitted with huge 18.4 R30 Goodyear tyres, the Bray is a beast and takes some shunting in tight spaces. The finished result is breath-taking when you consider that the tractor arrived on a pallet.

The Charnleys are always keen to hear from Bray owners and happy to help anyone with a restoration underway. They can be contacted at John Charnley & Sons, Marsh Lane, Brindle, Chorley, Lancs PR6 8NY. Telephone: 01254 854103 or visit the website: www.charnleys.com ∎

The Steiger Turbo Tiger was powered by a 320hp Cummins V8 engine, with a displacement of 903cu in. Photo: Peter D Simpson.

Key facts

Built:	North Dakota, USA
Engine:	V8-cyl Cummins VT-903
Power:	320hp
Chassis:	Articulated, four-wheel drive
Typical farm:	Large American arable

Lonely existence

While driving around America, Peter D Simpson caught up with Joe Stringer and his Steiger Tiger.

Hard at work near Box Elder, Montana, this c1973 Steiger Turbo Tiger is powered by a 320hp V8 engine. Built between 1973-74, the model uses a turbocharged Cummins VT-903 diesel unit, rated at 2,600rpm.

At the time of the photograph, the tractor had less than 5,000 hours on the clock and appeared in good condition for its age. It's worth remembering that due to the drier climate in North America, tractors do not deteriorate as much as European examples.

The tractor's owner, Joe Stringer, farms around 3,500 acres and crops 1,700 acres a year with either winter or spring wheat, depending on autumn moisture levels. Being a farmer in Montana can be a lonely kind of existence, but can have rich rewards if you get it right. To make a living you need vast acreages, as the land is not very fertile. ∎

The Rite tractor

Peter D Simpson takes a look at the history of the Rite tractor.

During 1945, brothers Dave and Jack Curtis started a farm implement business in Dutton, 30 miles north of Great Falls, Montana. Their first franchise was Oliver equipment, soon joined by other machinery.

Visiting a fellow dealership in eastern Montana during the spring of 1954, Jack Curtis obtained a brochure on the Wagner four-wheel drive articulated tractor, manufactured in Portland, Oregon.

The Curtis brothers became very interested and were invited to Portland for a demonstration.

The Wagner brothers (Walter, Elmer and Irvin) and J. Burke Long started developing the first true four-wheel drive articulated agricultural tractors during 1953/54. However, various engine and articulation problems had caused the company a dilemma.

The Curtis brothers, also pioneers of tractor design, were invited to assist the Wagner brothers with design improvements.

The introduction of the Wagner four-wheel drive range had marked the beginning of success for the true articulated tractor," says Dave Curtis. "We were given one of the first Wagner dealerships in the US and Canada. During that first year Jack and I sold 32 Wagner tractors."

Dave and his brother Jack helped the Wagner Brothers, but did not fully appreciate that these first tractors were not properly equipped for agricultural use.

They were not fitted with planetary axles and used Waukesha and Buda engines –

good engines for trucks, but not for farm tractors.

Dave Curtis said: "For years, we were making changeovers on the Wagner tractors, installing larger engines, altering transmissions and correcting driveline misalignment. Then a customer asked us to custom-build him a tractor of 425hp."

"Jack and I used common components in order to keep costs down, with parts and service readily available." That build was the beginning of Rite tractors, which were custom built for a niche market.

Dave Curtis adds: "In late 2002 a customer, Mervin Laughlin from Youngstown, Alberta became interested in manufacturing the Rite tractor again. In early 2003 Mervin and I decided to build a Rite tractor using existing components.

"Mervin designed a sloping hood that hinged forward from the front and a clear-vision Massey Ferguson cab that tilted to the right for easy access to the main components.

"We used a Michigan 290M frame, the axles were Clark 70,000lb, the engine a Detroit Diesel 60 Series rated at 460hp at 2,200rpm, the transmission was a Clark four-speed drop box with full power-shift and the whole machine was fitted onto four large-footprint Michelin 800/65x32 tyres.

"When we built the first Rite Tractor, we knew how to match horsepower to components and how to put weight in them to pull a wanted load. It takes weight to pull weight – there is no substitute. Large engines with small axles and transmissions don't work.

"We felt it was necessary to build on a good base, the axles, and if more power was needed it was comparatively easy to put in larger engines and transmissions.

"The weight ratio between the front and rear units is very important, usually 60 per cent front and 40 per cent rear, the load pulled then equalises the weight front and rear."

The Curtis brothers built enough weight into the Rite tractor. They used the correct sized tyres to cut down compaction and to aid traction and flotation.

Machinery manufacturer Loyd Richey had seen the new tractor at work during late 2003. He contacted Dave Curtis with a ➡

Key facts

Built:	Montana, USA
Engine:	Cummins or Detroit Diesel
Power:	Above 400hp
Chassis:	Articulated, four-wheel drive
Typical farm:	Large American arable

Above: Brothers Dave and Jack Curtis promoting their tractors at a Montana show in the 1970s.

Top: Each Rite tractor was different, custom built, unique to a particular farmer's requests. This 470 was built in 1992.

Left: Dave Curtis said: "We knew how to match horsepower to components and how to put weight in them to pull a wanted load. It takes weight to pull weight – there is no substitute."

"I have been close to the tractor business all these years and it seems to be the main interest keeping me busy. It is pleasing to note how farmers and operators still want a custom-built tractor and I am glad they have chosen the Rite brand."

In 1973 the Curtis brothers built their own Rite 425hp four-wheel drive articulating tractor, in the spring of 2004 86-year-old Dave Curtis finished and tested his 37th tractor, the 460hp 2460-D. He will have been in the four-wheel drive tractor business for 52 years, but it appears the Rite name will continue to flourish under the stewardship of Loyd Richey. ∎

view to start constructing Rite Tractors once again. Richey says "After extensive testing our new tractor, the Rite 2460-D, achieved a proven test performance second to none. Powered by a Detroit Diesel 60 Series engine rated at 460hp, it achieved success as the tractor of Olympic standard for the 21st century."

Dave added, "Richey has invested considerable resources including a new building to build the tractors in. I think it is good that a small name such as Rite can generate interest in the modern-day tractor world, especially when the giants have consolidated with only three major tractor manufactures remaining in North America."

Dave concluded: "Around twenty years ago chemical farming, lo-till and no-till farming systems limited the need for large horsepower tractors. As time goes by there will be a greater need for the large dependable four-wheel drive articulating tractor as labour is reduced and outputs from one man increase.

Built and tested in 2004, the 460hp Rite 2460-D is a friendly, safe, simple and efficient tractor designed to maximise profits and minimise down time with down-to-earth performance and versatility that won't break the bank. It is ideally suited for the open prairies of the northwest grain belt.

86 year-old Dave Curtis has been in the four-wheel drive tractor business for 52 years.

Robert says one of the biggest let-downs on the Crystal is the weak tin work so on all his tractors he has fitted front-end protection.

Key facts	
Built:	Brno, Czech Republic
Engine:	6-cyl Zetor 8601
Power:	120hp
Chassis:	Rigid, two-wheel drive
Typical farm:	European arable

Zetor's magic Crystals

Peter D Simpson talks to the Daly family about their tractors and finds that Zetors were ahead of their time, then behind the times.

During the 1960s the demand from farmers across Europe for a heavy, powerful range of tractors grew unabated. Zetor's existing range was insufficient for the expanding grain farms and in 1968 development of a second Unified Range of tractors (known as UR2) was completed and they were given a new name, the Zetor Crystal.

In 1970 the UR2 Crystal tractors were introduced to the UK market and featured the high technical standards that were required for modern large-scale farming, such as hydraulically-operated front-wheel drive, power-shift, and power take-off.

A standard feature on the Crystal was the world's first safety cab with an integrated roll-over protection structure mounted on silent blocks.

Zetor's engineers pioneered a revolutionary hitch-hydraulic draft system with its sensors on the lower link arms, a system not seen on any other tractor of that era. The new hydraulic system, called the Zetormatic, featured full-position, draft and mixed control.

The international Press acknowledged that the Zetor Crystal raised the technological standard of agricultural tractors to a higher level.

The first UR2 Crystals were the 8011 (two-wheel drive) and 8045 (four-wheel drive). They had the same 4.6-litre, four-cylinder engine with around 85hp at 2,200rpm.

These two models were followed three years later by the six-cylinder 12011 (two-wheel drive) and 12045 (four-wheel drive).

The Crystal was an affordable tractor with a wide range of standard features and high productivity, which made it a milestone in the history of tractor production. Many of

the features that Zetor offered as standard equipment were optional on the tractors of the competition, or weren't available at all.

During 1972, in official tests in Sweden, the Crystal was the world's first tractor to meet the N 85 noise level demands.

The tractors were ahead of their time in design and technology and were the favoured tractor of many European contractors and owners of large farms.

While the UR1 range of tractor was extensively modified and updated in order to keep up with modern tractor technology, the UR2 Crystal tractor remained virtually unchanged for almost 30 years.

Gradually the Crystal's popularity declined due to the increasing technology of its competitors.

One of the reasons for this decline was that manufacture was transferred from its parent factory in Brno to the ZTS factory in Northern Slovakia, where there was no ➡

research and development department.

This move was partly political – the jobs being moved from high-density employment areas to employment black spots throughout Eastern Europe – but the tractor continued to be built unchanged for too long.

A replacement for the Crystal range finally arrived during the mid-1990s, called the Forterra and brought Zetor back to the cutting edge of design and technology in agricultural tractors.

The Crystal is still produced in small numbers for the home market but no longer exported across Western Europe.

Robert Daly and his two sons, Joe and John, who farm in Ballysheal, Co Offaly, have used Crystals since 1977 when Robert started to replace his ageing Ford fleet with a brand new Zetor 8045 four-wheel drive, which they still use today.

He had been loyal to Ford tractors since 1946 in both his farming and silage contracting business. Running Fordson E27Ns and then the more modern Majors, there came a time in the mid-1970s when he required more power and he looked at the 94hp turbocharged Ford 7000.

The Daly family – Joe with his young son Robert on left, Robert senior centre and John on right.

But at the same time he drove a secondhand Zetor Crystal 8011, rated at 85hp from a naturally-aspirated engine.

Robert was so impressed with the Crystal's overall performance and weight distribution that he ended up purchasing a new four-

Daly fleet profile

	8011	8045	12011	12111
Produced	1968-84	1968-84	1974-84	1984-87
Built	1977	1977	1980	1984
Acquired	1978	1977	1993	2004
Engine	4-stroke, OHV diesel, liquid cooled, direct-injection			
Model	Z8001 4-cylinder	Z8001 4-cylinder	Z8601 6-cylinder	Z8601 6-cylinder
Power	85	85	120	120
Aspiration	Naturally-aspirated			

wheel drive Crystal 8045, rated at 85hp, and also the second hand two-wheel drive 8011 – both for the same price as the new Ford 7000 would have cost.

"Pound for pound the Crystal was far better value for money than the Ford. People told me the Zetor would have a very low trade-in value but I was not interested as I aimed to keep the tractors until they died and they are still running well nearly 30 years on" Robert explains.

"I used to run a Fordson Major fitted with a six-cylinder engine, giving out over 110hp, which was good for silage work and had great torque.

"The Zetor was a four-cylinder model with 20 less horsepower so I couldn't compare like for like but the Crystal could pull the forage harvest with ease and I was more than happy."

The tractors Robert had previously used had no cabs, just roll bars. Now he had a new tractor with a large, flat-deck, sealed cab, column gear change, power steering and self-adjusting brakes.

"I can remember other tractor dealers looking down on the Crystal with its flat deck cab and other improved features but it wasn't long before the competition followed suit. The Zetor cab was warm, big and roomy and way ahead of its time; no other tractor had such a good cab."

Robert found his new tractor was very easy to maintain and service with new parts easy to come by and reasonably priced as a good Zetor dealer network had been established across the Republic of Ireland.

"What I liked about the Crystal were the lift arms with bottom link sensors that put weight where it was needed, that is on to the ground, giving improved traction. The lift arms were telescopic, making it easier to couple on to the large heavy implements that were coming on to the market. ➡

The 1980 Zetor 12011, pulling a KRM Bredal fertiliser spreader, is ideal for grassland work, especially at silage time.

Right: Robert aboard a new Forterra 10641, demonstrated by Michael Brogan the local Zetor tractor dealer, with his trusted Crystal 12111 at the side.

Below: John tends to use the Crystal 12111 as a sprayer tractor on the farm and says this was the third ZTS tractor off the line, recognised by the higher cab.

"The tractor was very operator-friendly and fully roadworthy with lights, indicators and the like. There was nothing in Ireland available to even come close to this tractor for land cultivation work involving the link arms or drawbar work," says Robert.

By the early 1980s a compressor was fitted to the Crystal, enabling air brakes to be used and making roadwork much safer with a very efficient breaking system.

"The Crystal tractor was totally different to any of the other Zetors, being a higher-powered tractor with more weight. It was built stronger all round, especially around the back axle, and the gearbox was stronger, well suited for the higher power band and the heavier work rates expected form it.

"I had looked at a Crystal 12011, rated at 120hp, during the late 1980s but never managed to get one until 1993. When it was released into Ireland around 1978 no other tractor had such power and any available models were quickly snapped up.

"The Crystal became a top seller in Southern Ireland during 1988 and the top of the range Crystal 16045 at 160hp was a monster power house, always on top of its work. Most farmers today require a tractor in the 90-110hp bracket and the Zetor Crystal was and still is a favourite second tractor.

"I can't see any reason to change makes of tractors, I know the Crystals inside and out. I can easily work on them and the later models are just as user-friendly and easily maintained.

"I have always been happy with Zetor tractors and those we use on our farm today all have in excess of 10,000 hours on the clock. If a new Zetor Crystal were available today I would buy one but, as there isn't, the tractors we work with have plenty of life left in them and they have been very reliable and cost efficient." ■

Passion for big kit

With six articulated tractors under his belt, Scott Thomas has plenty of power in his fleet. Howard Sherren talked to him.

Scott Thomas loves big and unusual tractors but he doesn't work in agriculture; he is actually employed in the telecoms industry. His family, however, still farms at Maiden Law Farm, a small sheep farm in Maiden Law, Co Durham.

Long gone are the days of working the fields for crops and the only thing to be harvested now is hay for their flock of rare sheep. The sheep are Herdwicks, which are a hardy breed and mainly a hobby for Scott and his father Dixon.

Dixon drives heavy plant for a living, while Scott's work takes him across the UK and Europe, spending long periods away from home.

The main movers on the farm are an International Harvester 785 and a Massey Ferguson 1200, mainly because the rest of the fleet is far from practical. Scott is a true believer in keeping all the machines in their working clothes.

They have recently converted the old silage pit into a tractor shed to get machines under cover so they can start carrying out a few jobs on them. They also have an interesting array of construction equipment as part of their collection.

The MF 1200 is one of the key players on the farm thanks to its size and ➡

In original form this John Deere 8430 has 5,500 hours on the clock.

Key facts

Built:	Iowa, USA
Engine:	6-cyl John Deere 6466
Power:	209hp
Chassis:	Articulated, four-wheel drive
Typical farm:	Large arable

manoeuvrability. It was bought locally in bits after the shaft between the engine and the gearbox broke. The owner was quoted a staggering £1,000 just for labour, on top of the cost of a replacement shaft, so it was sold.

The Thomas's hauled it back and put it back together with a combine engine, a Perkins 6.354, and a repaired shaft to get it back to working order. This engine offers plenty of poke and the tractor remains very useable for farming jobs.

Another Massey Ferguson in the fleet is a Caterpillar-powered 1505 model, which came from tractor dealer Robert Fearnley in Norfolk. It has clocked less than 3,500 hours and had been parked up for 15 years as the previous owner had sold off land for housing and didn't need it anymore.

It is on single wheels, which makes moving it easier, has a three-point linkage – which makes it a little more useable – but there is no pto. It sometimes gets 'sticky' on the steering which Scott believes is because of the over-complicated way in which the hydraulics for the steering are routed. This is a common problem on 1505s and one day they will simply bypass the compensating and balancing circuit and install a small, separate tank for the steering.

Scott's interest in unusual tractors doesn't stop there. An old imported Versatile 500

The rubber-tracked TM 250 crawler is a rare beast, being one of only a few 250 models produced.

was in excellent original order but made way for a rare rubber-tracked Track-Marshall TM 250. He admits this was probably a mistake as the Versatile was a lovely machine, but he is adamant he will get another one some day, possibly a 900 Series with the Cummins 903 V8.

The TM 250 was one of four larger TM 200 crawlers, which were produced for a short period in the 1990s. This TM 250 was once owned by Claydon's who converted her to CAT Challenger running gear when the original tracks and running gear were not up to scratch. Many models were converted, so

In excess of 1,000 horsepower, Scott's fleet is a mixed bag of prairie monsters.

This Muir-Hill is an odd machine to have in the fleet but is the second 171 model to be built.

Bought unseen when Scott was working in Holland is the second ever Muir-Hill 171 Series 1. Found at S R Haylock Machinery in Cambridgeshire, the Perkins 540 V8 tractor is a bit of a mess but the important bit is the serial number, according to Scott.

"She runs well mechanically but, as can be seen, needs a serious restoration," he said. "There is a three-point hitch but no pto as these were an independent, hydraulic-powered unit. I may get one for it some time as it will be a handy-sized machine when finished."

Carrying on with the MF theme, Scott found himself a giant 4840 model, again supplied by Robert Fearnley. It is powered by a Cummins V8 903 engine, which has covered an impressive 12,000 hours but is still very straight and running extremely well. As with all the other machines it is original and ideally in need of a coat of paint, but the family will probably wait for the shed to be finished.

They have found the 4840 is excellent at pulling out tree stumps with its massive 30.5-inch wide single wheels and they had it discing alongside a neighbour's FW-30. Despite being down on the FW for power, it didn't disgrace itself. Scott feels the 4840's cab is superior to both the Steiger and the Ford FW, providing considerably more space and comfort. ➡

it is now rare to find one with the originals still in place.

Other desirable models on the farm include a battered and bruised County 1124 fitted with a turbocharged truck engine which is believed to be 140hp. Scott has a Bomford blade to fit on the front and a large

hydraulic winch to go on the back to make this machine a little more useable.

"She is a very good runner with a frightening road speed," said Scott. "Currently she is stuck between gears and needs a little work in the clutch area but I will get her sorted shortly."

Scott's latest project was this Steiger Tigress, which was bought in bits from Amtrac, the original creator of this prototype.

A couple of different shades of green artic feature in the Thomas collection, from both the Deere and Steiger stables. Robert Fearnley supplied Scott with a 210hp John Deere 8430 with duals all-round and 5,500 hours on the clock.

"She just fits through our narrow 12-foot gate," said Scott. "It's in good original condition and I am probably not going to paint her any time soon."

It comes with the usual blistering around the windows in the cab and a bit on the rear mudguards but this isn't a major problem to Scott.

It came with a Ransomes 16-foot disc harrow which, thankfully, puts all its horses to work when he gets to use it. In recent years he has had a few problems keeping the dual wheels attached after one of the hubs broke and a wheel parted company – scary stuff!

In a lighter shade of green, Scott's Steiger Cougar III uses a 3306 Caterpillar straight-six set at 270 horsepower. However, she looks a bit worse for wear and is in need of shot-blasting and painting but, despite this, the engine runs sweetly and it drives remarkably well.

Scott said: "The Steiger gives a better gear change than the Massey Fergusons. This one came from John Deere dealer Sharmans at Grantham and I saw it driving past one day and just bought it over the phone."

When he went to look at it, the fitter thought that it was a Cummins engine. That didn't instil Scott with any confidence when they couldn't tell the difference, but it turned out OK and wasn't a concern.

Scott fitted the Steiger with a set of duals but, with them fitted, it is too wide to go through the gate so they have to be removed if the tractor leaves the farm. The Cougar is a good pattern for Scott's latest project, the 525hp Tigress tractor.

The Tigress 525 monster came from John Nicholson at Amtrac in North Yorkshire. It was the prototype for his Lioness range of machines back in the Nineties. It was originally built as 470hp and ran for 600 hours as a prototype. It was too expensive to get the cab tested as a one-off so John dismantled it.

He had started thinking of putting the V12 3412 Caterpillar engine back into the chassis but after some calculations he thought he

wouldn't get the power transferred to the wheels effectively, so shelved it.

Scott's machine has a brand-new Caterpillar 3408 V8 engine set at 525 horsepower. To withstand the extra power they beefed up the axles, using Ford FW-60 casings fitted to a two-speed differential supplied by John.

They also had to extend the chassis by two feet for better airflow and an appropriate engine and transmission fit. The transmission was an Allison auto box and easily capable of handling high power.

Further modifications were made to the tin work, and a linkage was fitted, along with four spools at the rear. This was an impressive build, especially as Scott and his dad were on a budget and only working weekends with 60-year old lifting equipment for the vital moving jobs.

Scott has a spare Steiger chassis and cab, so hopes to be able to build a V12 Detroit twin turbo, supercharged two-stroke-powered tractor with Clark axles from a Euclid dump truck. Working with John at Amtrac they will have some fun with this 500hp project. ■

A-C 'Queen Marys'

Peter D Simpson met up with one of the last working Allis-Chalmers prairie tractors in New York State.

The Allis-Chalmers 7000 series of two-wheel drive tractors was introduced in 1973; they were designed from scratch and known as a 'clean sheet design'. They looked totally different to any previous A-C tractor.

Once all the tooling was in place and production of the two-wheel drive tractors was fully underway at West Allis, Wisconsin, the management team settled down to building the company's first genuine four-wheel drive tractor, as they needed to replace the bought-in Steiger 440 (Bearcat) of which remarkably over 1,000 were sold in Allis colours, and many were exported to Australia until June 1976.

The company used many power-train components from the two-wheel drive 7000 Series, needing only a two-speed transfer box and a two-speed front differential housing coupled to the Power-Director transmission, which produced 20 forward and four reverse gears.

However the rear end was all new, along with the saddle fuel tanks, hydraulics, and modified electrics. In all 73 per cent of all parts were sourced 'in house.'

In 1975 the 7580 prairie tractor was nearly ready, using the 7080's 3750 Mk2 222hp engine, producing 153.7 drawbar horsepower.

Many other components were familiar to the A-C user, like the cab and bonnet. Introduced to the farmer in the American bicentennial year of 1976, the tractor made some friends, and by the end of production in 1981 some 2,622 had been made, more than its larger brother.

You could roughly tell the year of the 7580 by the colour of the frame, axles, engine, transmission and rear hitch, which from 1975 to 1977 was a brown-maroon colour. In 1978 Allis-Chalmers changed the colour to black. ➡

Fitted on duals all round the Allis-Chalmers 8550 has standard 18.4x38 tyres; the 20-forward, 4-reverse transmission allows for speeds of 1.9mph in first gear to 18.7mph in top at 2,500rpm.

Key facts

Built:	Wisconsin, USA
Engine:	6-cyl Allis-Chalmers 6120T
Power:	305hp
Chassis:	Articulated, four-wheel drive
Typical farm:	Large American arable

A-C 8550 serial numbers

1977	1001-1082	**1980**	1553-1722
1978	1083-1341	**1981**	1723-2021
1979	1342-1552		

However, in the late 1970s the tractor world was one of 'keeping up with the Jones's,' and Allis-Chalmers did not sit down and fall asleep as it had done previously, as the larger and more successful 8550 model came off the Wisconsin production line in 1976.

The platform was the same as the earlier and smaller 7580, but the monster had more power and the engine was based on the Allis-Chalmers HD-21 844cu in crawler engine.

The engine was given a shorter stroke, which increased the revs, and produced

305hp on test. The in-line six-cylinder, 12-litre, 731cu in engine was given two small turbochargers and two exhaust manifolds and silencers. The marketing team affectionately named the tractors 'Queen Marys' because of the two prominent chimneys!

The transmission was similar to its smaller brother, but with beefed-up gears to handle the extra horsepower. Similarly the hydraulics were up-rated.

The cab and fuel tanks were common to both tractors and the frame was black on the production models.

Like all big prairie tractors maintenance costs could be high, and the problem was possibly the engine, but like all Allis-Chalmers machines of the time they were ➡

A 1981 305hp Allis-Chalmers 8550 seen working in Perry, New York State, USA, in the spring of 2004, one of the last of its type still at work.

Above: The fully independent 1,000rpm power take-off was rated at 250hp. A category III or IV three-point linkage was an optional extra and with external lift rams the linkage could lift 4.4 tons – adequate for most farming operations.

Below: The A-C 8550 had a smaller brother in the 222hp 7580, possibly a better and more reliable tractor than the model shown here.

normally very reliable. Surprisingly only 2,021 were built by the time the company introduced its replacement, the 4W-305, in 1981.

Things were getting tough for Allis-Chalmers by then and in 1985, with major losses posted, on 6 December the Wisconsin, West Allis plant was closed, and the Allis-Chalmers farm division was sold to Klöckner-Humboldt-Deutz of West Germany. It turned out to be a major disaster, but out of the ashes in 1990 came AGCO-Allis, but that's another story.

The Allis-Chalmers prairie line is nearly but not quite forgotten, a few Queen Marys live on, but only just… ∎

Specifications

Produced	1977-81
Engine	A-C 6120T
Power (hp)	305
Max power @ (rpm)	2,500
Cylinders	6
Aspiration	Twin turbo
Displacement (cu in)	731
Fuel capacity (gallons)	141
Standard transmission	20 forward, 4 reverse
Power take-off (rpm/hp)	1,000/250
Top speed (mph)	18.7
Lift capacity (tons)	4.4
Turning circle to centre line (ft)	17
Length (in)	285
Wheelbase (in)	126
Height to top of cab (in)	139
Weight (tons)	12½
Standard tyre size	18.4 R38

Ford's big beasts

Ford's FW Series tractors are now considered as a cheap source of power. Howard Sherren advises on buying one.

I t is almost 30 years since Ford launched its first artic-steer tractor, the FW-30. Built by Steiger at its Fargo factory in North America, it was the largest tractor the company had produced.

The FW range was based on the Steiger Panther III, which meant an excellent artic pedigree.

The high horsepower range was unveiled in 1977, but it wasn't until December 1978 at the Smithfield Show that the 295hp FW-30 was launched. Priced at just over £40,000, it wasn't cheap but around half a dozen were sold in the UK in the first year of production.

As demand for more power increased, a larger model was introduced. The 335hp FW-60 was again first sighted at Smithfield in December 1980. Priced only slightly higher than the FW-30 at £45,000, the FW-60's price-to-horsepower ratio was lower than Ford's smaller tractors.

Sales of both models increased dramatically and, by 1982, 48 tractors were working on UK farms, but it soon became a challenge to sell FWs as the demand for these prairie monsters fell and used examples were difficult to re-home due to the presence of higher horsepower rigid-frame tractors.

A revised version of the FW-60 was launched in May 1984 to create more interest in the range: the biggest differences were a 325hp Cummins six-cylinder turbo engine, Dana axles and square lights. A year later an Allison 10-speed automatic transmission became an option, which saw the price hiked up to nearly £70,000.

After selling 145 tractors in the UK, 1987 saw Ford stop production when it purchased the Versatile company and began producing the 946 model, which featured the same Cummins engine as the existing FW-60.

Steiger was then sold to Case IH which started producing its Steiger-based 9100 Series. ➡

Key facts

Built:	North Dakota, USA
Engine:	V8-cyl Cummins V-903
Power:	295hp
Chassis:	Articulated, four-wheel drive
Typical farm:	Large arable

The Ford FW-30 was originally sold with dual wheels, but it was common to see singles fitted as farmers looked to reduce width.

Cummins V8 903 supplied the power on the early tractors. Engines should be good for 7,000 hours, possibly more. Top end tuning is advisable every 1,500 hours after 4,000 hours.

Engine

Both tractors were fitted with the 903cu in Cummins V8 engine, producing 295hp in the FW-30 and 335hp in the FW-60 using a turbocharger. The rated speed was at 2,600 rpm and maximum torque of the FW-30 was 849Nm found at 1,800rpm.

The engine bore was 140mm with a stroke of 121mm and each cylinder had four valves. When the revised FW-60 was introduced in 1984, a 325hp, six-cylinder Cummins engine with a turbo and after-cooler was used instead. Producing 10hp less with two cylinders fewer, the newer engine still provided plenty of power.

As with many of the larger engines, plenty of electrical power is needed for cranking. The tractors are fitted with four batteries, which need to be in good order, especially in cold weather. The engines will normally last for around 7,000 hours. It is a good idea to have the engine's top-end tuned overhauled every 1,500 hours after they have done 4,000 hours.

Transmission

A 20-forward and four-reverse manual gearbox, manufactured by Spicer, was fitted as standard in the United Kingdom. A two-speed transfer case was used, which doubled the usual ten-forward and two-reverse speeds.

Five gears in two ranges with a splitter gave speeds from 3.38kph up to 34.75kph, adequate for a tractor that weighs over 10 tons.

The later 'automatic' versions, released in 1985, had an Allison 10-speed automatic transmission. There were five speeds in each of the two ranges (high and low) and it was a similar principal to driving an automatic car.

Transmissions are usually trouble-free for 5,000 to 7,000 hours on the FW-30, 4,000 to 6,000 hours on the FW-60 and double these values for the automatic transmission.

If the tractor has a gearbox problem, the most likely fault is that it will primarily jump out of third gear, then second and then reverse.

Rear linkage

Although these large prairie tractors were designed for drawbar work, many of the operations in the UK involved using the three-point linkage.

The top link casting was redesigned and stabilisers were developed after larger mounted equipment caused linkage failure. Dowdeswell helped produce the uprated linkage as it was mainly its cultivation equipment which could harness the power of the FW.

The lift capacity was a respectable 5,670kg, enough to hoist most mounted and semi-mounted implements off the ground. The hitch was category III and had 'Quick' hitch as standard.

Not many problems will be encountered here as the majority of work is likely to have been on the drawbar. However, many linkages in the UK were often abused (when using sub-soilers for example) so it is necessary to check for wear in joints and stress fractures.

History

1977: Ford FW tractor unveiled to the world.

1978 (Dec): 295hp FW-30 UK launch at Smithfield Show.

1980 (Dec): 335hp FW-60 UK launch at Smithfield Show.

1982: FW-30 production stopped, last of FW-30s arrive by 1984.

1984 (May): 325hp Cummins-powered FW-60 launched.

1985: FW-60 Automatic launched.

1987: Production ceased as Ford acquired Versatile Company and Steiger bought by Case IH.

Contacts

Midwest Machinery
Big tractors and parts
Moreton-in-Marsh, Gloucestershire
01608 651874
www.midwest-machinery.com

Amtrac
Rebuilt big tractors and parts
Bedale, North Yorkshire
01677 422158
www.amtrac.co.uk

The FW-30 was rated at 295hp in the UK instead of the specified 265hp. The engine was the same as the FW-40, so modifications to the fuel pump gave 30 extra horsepower for the UK.

Hydraulics

The FW Series tractors use an open-centre hydraulic system, which is powered by a 113.6 litre/min gear pump. Four remote valves came as standard across the range and offered a maximum output of 75.4 litre/min.

The system runs at 2,250psi and also powers the two, substantial, 88.9mm diameter steering rams. The hydraulic and steering reservoir hold 94.3 litres of oil, more than enough for all operations.

Axles & brakes

The early tractors used Steiger-Raba axles with single planetary hubs, made in Hungary. In 1984, when the range was revised, Dana axles were used as an alternative.

The brakes were multiple dry discs with hydraulic actuation. Four 228.6mm discs, located in the transfer case, brought the tractor to a halt. The park brake was cable-operated and an emergency brake was also fitted.

Brakes and axles rarely gave trouble as the brakes were never really used and their performance was very poor. Signs of oil leaking from seals should be checked as it is a good indication of the condition of the bearings. The more oil you see, the worse the bearing condition.

Seals and bearings can still be easily obtained; one bearing and seal can be purchased for around £300.

Centre pivots can also show signs of wear from increased use of the linkage in the ➥

United Kingdom. To check for wear in the pivot, the tractor should be placed in reverse and the clutch released quickly while having a firm grasp of the steering wheel. If worn, the back of the cab and front pivot should lift and a clunking noise will be heard. A pivot can be easily repaired.

Cab

Ford used the existing Steiger cab, which was kitted out with all the essentials. Forty-one square feet of tinted glass gave great visibility and, with sound insulation, air conditioning and stereo radio, the cab made for a desirable operator environment.

Two front work lights and four rear lights were fitted as standard which, together with the four headlights, made night work easy.

Excellent build quality means there is little to cause concern here. Many interiors have seen a lot of abuse and the cab cladding can take a beating, but nearly all cab parts are still available. Check for rot in the roof gutters and corroding drill holes on top.

Dials and switches are easy to read and the adjustable steering column works well.

Two Ford FW-30s, once belonging to Midwest Machinery, found new homes in Yorkshire and Lapland – where demand for simple high-horsepower tractors is on the increase.

Spool levers are very well located and close to the driver's right-hand side. ➡

Specifications

	FW-30	FW-60
Engine	Cummins V-903	Cummins V-903
Power (hp)	295	335
Max power @ (rpm)	2,600	2,600
Max torque @ (rpm)	1,800	1,800
Cylinders	8	8
Displacement (cc)	14,719	14,719
Bore (mm)	140	140
Stroke (mm)	121	121
Fuel capacity (litres)	850	850
Standard transmission	20 forward, 4 reverse	20 forward, 4 reverse
Lift capacity (kg)	5,670	5,670
Turning radius (mm)	6,000	6,270
Length (mm)	6,780	6,780
Width (mm)	3,663	4,166
Weight (kg)	11,485	11,874
Standard tyre size	18.4 R38	24.5 R32
Cab	Steiger	Steiger

Rear linkage was capable of lifting 5,670kg, but many linkages were abused in the UK with heavy mounted implements. Photo: Peter D Simpson.

Driving

To board the monster of a machine, one has to ascend five very wide and user-friendly steps. Once elevated into the seat of the FW-30, the benefit of 41sq ft of tinted glass soon becomes apparent.

Starting the engine on a cold morning appears to be a problem, but after about 10 seconds of cranking the engine bursts into life. The bark of the V8 is certainly an impressive sound.

The driving position is good, with a fair view of the dials and warning lights and the adjustable steering wheel is excellent.

The gear selection is made with a centre-mounted gear lever which can hinder entering and exiting the cab. The range lever is also a stretch to the right of the dash, but normally not many gear changes are

required on a tractor of this size so it needn't be a problem. Spool and linkage levers could not be in a better place than to the driver's right.

The large clutch pedal is soft and effortless to use and selecting a gear feels very similar to that of a smaller Ford tractor from the same era. Once moving, changing gear smoothly can be mastered.

Steering is easy and sensitive; the steering lock is also particularly good for a tractor of this size.

Brakes are a weak point as they feel very spongy and ineffective.

Heater and cooling controls to the left of the dash are very simple to use, as is the radio located in the front of the roof. Two drink can holders on the dash are a useful addition.

Verdict

The best way to describe the FW is as a dependable, value-for-money tractor that would provide a simple power source for many arable cultivation techniques.

High-houred models can cause problems but some tractors have worked 18,000 hours without any major internal work yet.

Although CNH can only offer limited consumables, nearly all other major parts are available though specialists such as Midwest Machinery. The FWs were based on the Steiger Panther Series III and IV, so many of the parts are the same. Parts are now therefore on the shelf at Versatile and are easily accessible.

* With thanks to Wayne Middleton at Ernest Doe and Son and Tim Ingles at Midwest Machinery. ∎

Farming in Montana

Peter D Simpson visits the Williams brothers to see how their tractor requirements have changed over the years.

In the United Kingdom we all too often see high-horsepower tractors replacing labour on the farm. Going back a decade or two, 1,000-acre plus arable farms would have had three or four tractor drivers operating tractors in the 100-125hp range.

Now probably one or two operators drive machines of 300hp or more. The Williams Brothers from Big Sandy in Montana are not replacing manpower for horsepower, they are just simple increasing power. Three tractors with a total rating of nearly 2,000hp undertake all the fieldwork on a 10,000-acre cropping program.

Robert and Randy Williams have become a worldwide name amongst enthusiasts of big articulated tractors. For five years the brothers have operated the worlds largest agricultural tractor, the Big Bud 16V747 rated at just over 900hp and weighing in at nearly 58 tons.

During late 2002 this tractor with its massive Detroit Diesel engine was laid up due to a blown engine. The damaged engine was replaced with a similar Detroit 16V92T engine, the original engine has now been refurbished and is being stored as a standby.

The Detroit engine has 16 cylinders in a V configuration; fitted with dual turbochargers the tractor was originally rated at 760-engine hp, when the brothers refurbished the tractor in 1978 the engine was opened up to a colossal 900hp.

The 747 undertook all the field cultivations on the farm with an 80ft Friggstad light chisel plough cultivator working in front of two Case 4994 tractors. Each Case tractor pulled a John Deere 9400 60ft box seeder. Together they were capable of planting around 600 acres of wheat in a ten-hour day, including fill-ups.

The two Case 4994 rigid frame all-wheel steer tractors were Case's largest rigid frame tractors when built between 1984 and 1988.

A V8 Saab-Scania turbocharged diesel engine produced 400-engine hp with 344hp at the pto. Both Case tractors came to a sudden end just as winter seeding in 2003 ➡

Left: Angus Paterson meets the Williams brothers on a Tractor & Machinery Holiday Club visit to the farm, with the biggest 1970s tractor in the world standing behind. Photo: Peter Love.

Below: Randy and Robert Williams' pride and joy, the 58-ton, 900hp Big Bud 16V-747.

Key facts

Built:	Montana, USA
Engine:	V16-cyl Detroit Diesel 16V92T
Power:	900hp
Chassis:	Articulated, four-wheel drive
Typical farm:	Large American arable

This Case 4994 was destroyed by fire. Also in the line-up is the Williams' 1972 Case Agri-King 1070, a David Brown 1212 and the tractor that started it all for the family – a 1935 Case L. Photo: Peter Love.

was about to commence; the engine blew up on one and that was totally beyond repair, a couple of days later the second Case caught fire. It had been parked on some seeded land after a day's work and next morning it was found as a burned-out wreck.

Replacement tractors had to be found. The brothers travelled 50 miles north to Havre, the home of Big Bud tractors. Robert

The Williams brothers' Big Bud 600/50 is fitted with triple wheels all-round. The brothers run three Big Bud tractors with a total power rating just short of 2,000hp!

Until 2003, 10,000 acres were worked and seeded with 1,700hp in three tractors, two Case 4994s and a Big Bud 16V-747. The two seeders covered 120ft and the cultivator 80ft.

and Randy met with Ron Harmon, who used to build Big Bud tractors, and explained their predicament to him.

Two Big Bud tractors were quickly found, a 1980 Series 3 450/50 fitted on dual wheels all round and a 1981 600/50 fitted on triples all round. The 450 and 600 numbers denote horsepower from Cummins KTA-1150 six-cylinder engines respectively, the 50 prefix denoting Twin Disc Power-shift transmissions.

The older John Deere box seeders were becoming expensive to keep going so the brothers decided to purchase two replacement seeders. This time they chose the Flexi-Coil air seeders with grain cart and tool bar frame.

The two Flexi-Coil seeders are each 57ft wide, the brothers say that with a larger seed capacity in the air cart and an easier-to-pull machine they can seed the same acreage if not slightly more than they could do with the older Case tractors and box seeders.

Gabe, Randy's son, has now joined the team and loves driving one of the Big Bud tractors, usually the 450/50 fitted with a V8 Detroit Diesel pumping out 450 engine horsepower.

Gabe says if he plants around 350-400 acres of wheat in a 10-hour shift he feels he has done a good day's work. ■

This chaser bin is the perfect partner for the Williams' combine fleet. Photo: Peter Love.

Supersize me

Peter D Simpson on the biggest Massey Fergusons of them all.

During the mid-1970s Massey Ferguson recognised a growing need in America for larger, high horsepower, four-wheel drive articulated tractors.

The 1500 and 1800 Series had proved popular around the world but were simply too small. MF could not make them more powerful to compete with the majors like John Deere, Steiger and Versatile.

But the 4000 Series of articulated tractors made the company very competitive and a leader in the field. The MF 4800 and 4840 tractors were introduced in the autumn of 1978 and the more powerful 4880 in November 1979. The 4900, the highest powered in the series, was released in the spring of 1980.

The 4900 was the largest tractor built by MF and, being rated at 375hp, only the Steiger Tiger 450 at 450hp could beat it. The four 4000 Series tractors placed Massey

Ferguson in an excellent position in the very competitive four-wheel drive market.

The Massey Ferguson sales pitch at the time commented: "The Massey Ferguson 4000 Series four-wheel drive tractors are a superb blend of power and manoeuvrability. They give you the necessary horsepower to pull big implements with ease. But they also give you the many features you need to work in a variety of situations. Whether you farm thousands of acres of wheat, a few hundred acres of row crops or grow rice on

A Cummins V-903 engine, rated at 320-engine horsepower, nestles under the bonnet of the MF 4840.

Left: With an 18-speed transmission with a 3-speed shift-on-the-go, speeds ranged from 2.4mph to 19.2mph at 2,600rpm.

The 4000 Series tractors boasted roomy cabs with maximum operator comfort and convenience and excellent visibility (provided by an enormous 52sq ft of glass) compared to most of the opposition. Described as a roomy new command module, the cabs were by far the biggest on the market and many farmers who have built their own tractors and conversions have used the cab from the 4000 Series.

A major selling point into all agricultural operations – and a first on the American market – was the electronic three-point hitch system that offered more precise implement control.

Previously, matching implement working depth to varying soil or field conditions had caused numerous problems but, with the new system, constant draft load could be maintained when moving from one soil condition to another and this meant increased tractor efficiency.

The new electronically-controlled three-point hitch provided positive position control, full draft control or a combination of the two.

The MF 4800 and 4840 had a lift capacity of 11,000 pounds (4.91 tons) and the MF 4880 and 4900 a lift capacity of 13,000 pounds (5.8 tons).

The largest Massey Ferguson tractor in the four-wheel drive articulated range was the MF 5200, introduced in 1989 and produced until 1991.

McConnell Tractors, of North Carolina, had purchased the four-wheel drive tractor division of the Massey Combine Corporation and built the MF 5200 tractor that Massey Ferguson marketed under its banner. ➡

Key facts

Built:	Ontario, Canada
Engine:	V8-cyl Cummins V-903
Power:	265hp
Chassis:	Articulated, four-wheel drive
Typical farm:	Large American arable

the Delta, these tractors will fit into your operation."

All four tractors used the same V8 diesel engine, the Cummins V-903, the 903 denoting 903 cubic inches displacement. The two smaller tractors used the naturally-aspirated engine while the two larger models were turbocharged.

The rugged 18-speed transmission was standard on all four models with three-speed shift-on-the-go to provide the speed and power ranges needed to handle any situation. Working speeds were from 2.4mph to a top road speed of 19.2mph at 2,600rpm when fitted on 23.1x34 dual wheels all round. The extra large heavy-duty clutch consisted of four big 14-inch wet discs, providing plenty of contact area for long life and efficient power transfer.

A sales brochure for the MF 4000 Series.

J Ward McConnell began building the MF 5200 at a time when sales of the articulated tractor across America had risen by 53 per cent over the previous year. McConnell believed this 390-engine horsepower tractor could reduce farming costs and place the company in a strong position for further development.

The joint build and marketing agreement between McConnell and MF called for McConnell to manufacture two articulated four-wheel drive tractors in the 300-400hp

Opposite page, top: The Massey Ferguson 4000 Series is equally suited for drawbar and three-point hitch work.

Right: The MF 5200, rated at 390hp, was powered by a Detroit Diesel 12.7-litre engine.

Below: The articulated centre pivot design allowed the tractor to pivot 42° in either direction, giving a tight turning radius of 17 feet to centre line.

range to be supplied exclusively to, and distributed by, the MF dealer network under the Massey Ferguson name.

The MF 5200 range was an upgraded version of the MF 4000 Series. The body was restyled to take McConnell's larger engine but the operator cab remained virtually the same.

The MF 5200 was offered with two different engines types. The 12.7 litre Detroit Diesel Series 60 engine was an in-line, six-cylinder, turbocharged air-to-air, charge-cooled engine, producing 390hp at 2,100 rpm. The in-line six-cylinder turbocharged after-cooled Cummins NTA 855 engine produced 375hp at 2,100 rpm.

A choice of two transmissions was offered: a 12-speed manual or 12-speed full power-shift, the Twin Disc Power Commander.

It is interesting to note how big the operator cab was. Promotional material of the day said the ergonomically-designed cab featured a microwave oven to provide warm meals and hot beverages so that the operator could work longer hours and an ice chest could keep drinks cold and fresh on hot days. Other features included ➡

stereo cassette radio, air cushioned seat, air conditioning, tinted glass and much more besides.

After the 5200 deal with Massey Ferguson ended in 1991, McConnell Tractors introduced three new yellow-liveried models.

The Marc 900 produced 320hp and the Marc 1000 425hp and were for general agriculture operations, while the third model, the McConnell Marc 1000LL, rated at 390hp, was designed for land levelling operations. These new tractors were basically the same as the red MF 5200 units that McConnell previously built.

The Marc 900 and Marc 1000 both used a Detroit Series 60 six-cylinder turbo-charged and air-to-air charge-cooled diesel engine with 677 and 774 cubic inch displacement respectively. Transmission was a 12-speed manual on the Marc 900 and Marc 1000; the Marc 1000LL had a power-shift transmission, ideally suited to land levelling operations.

* Ref: *Ultimate Tractor Power volume 2*, Peter D Simpson – Japonica Press.

Specifications

Model	Produced	Engine	Power
Massey Ferguson			
4800	1978-1986	Cummins V8	225hp @ 2,600rpm
4840	1978-1986	Cummins V8	265hp @ 2,600rpm
4880	1979-1986	Cummins V8	320hp @ 2,600rpm
4900	1980-1986	Cummins V8	375hp @ 2,600rpm
5200	1989-1991	Detroit Diesel in-line 6-cylinder	390hp @ 2,100rpm
		Cummins Diesel in-line 6-cylinder	375hp @ 2,100rpm
McConnell-Marc			
900	1991-1994	Detroit Diesel in-line 6-cylinder	320hp @ 2,100rpm
1000	1991-1994	Detroit Diesel in-line 6-cylinder	425hp @ 2,100rpm
1000LL	1991-1994	Detroit Diesel in-line 6-cylinder	390hp @ 2,100rpm

McConnell-Marc tractors

Ward McConnell.

The McConnell-Marc 1000 was based on the McConnell-built Massey Ferguson 5200 Series.

Ward McConnell grew up in New York State on the family's 40-cow dairy farm. It was here that he grew to respect farm machinery and understand the need for power and stability as he drove the family's Allis-Chalmers WC over their hilly farm.

During 1956, after leaving the army, Ward McConnell opened his first tractor dealership, signing an Oliver franchise and opening the McConnell Motor Company.

It had always been his ambition to design and build his own agricultural machinery and he sold off his dealership in early 1961 and formed the McConnell Manufacturing Company Inc.

Over the next 20 years he was among the front-runners of those producing agricultural equipment in America.

In 1985, McConnell purchased the Marshall Tractor Company, of Gainsborough, England, and then sold the company on again as his interest lay in designing a high horsepower tractor.

It was in 1988 that he acquired the build rights to the Massey Ferguson 4000 Series tractors and decided to upgrade the power and options of the MF 4000 Series to create the 5000 Series.

It had taken Ward McConnell 30 years to realise his dream and produce his lifetime's ambition, his first tractor, the articulated four-wheel drive Massey Ferguson 5200.

The Allis-Gleaner Corporation (AGCO) purchased the McConnell tractor operation in 1994 and the McConnell-Marc 900 and 1000 tractors were restyled, updated and became the AGCO Star range of tractors in late 1995. ■

With the necessary horsepower and correct weight balance on all wheels, the MF 4000 Series had great traction to pull all types of implements.

Australian Colossus

There aren't many high-horsepower tractors with a two-wheel drive chassis, but Peter D Simpson managed to find one in New South Wales.

Until you have visited the wide-open countryside of Australia, it is hard to comprehend the vastness of the wheat-growing areas more commonly referred to as 'broadacre farming country'. It is in the southern states of this vast continent where some of the world's largest tractors still work, often in total isolation.

Australian-built four-wheel drive articulated tractors such as the Acremaster at 525hp, the Baldwin at 600hp and the Waltanna at 400hp were and still are some of the largest, most powerful tractors ever built; all were powered by dependable Cummins engines. Therefore it is not surprising to find the world's largest two-wheel drive tractor, the Upton HT-14/350, still hard at work in New South Wales.

Much of the Australian countryside is unforgiving, years of drought produce virtually no crops unless the land is irrigated; the temperatures get so hot during the day that the corn stops growing; if the wind blows, go inside as the dry dust just cuts into the skin.

Despite this, many farmers and machinery manufacturers have a successful track record. Two such people are Carl Upton, whose claim to fame is the Upton tractor; the other is Harold Cary whose farm covers 23,000 acres.

In the early 1960s Arthur Upton and his brothers ran a general engineering firm in Corowa on the Murray River in New South Wales. Among other lines the brothers were dealing in second-hand army tanks. They decided to strip one of these machines down to build an agricultural tractor from the various components.

In 1978 the tractor sold for $70,000 Australian, representing a cost of $200 for each horsepower produced, described at the time as the cheapest power available in Australia for farming.

Key facts

Built:	New South Wales, Australia
Engine:	6-cyl Cummins NTA855
Power:	350hp
Chassis:	Rigid, two-wheel drive
Typical farm:	Large Australian arable

Fabricator George Tobias on the platform with designer Carl Upton in 1978, with their creation that gained the title of the world's largest two-wheel drive production tractor.

'Heavy Harry' was the result, a 170hp supercharged two-wheel drive tractor with 20 forward speeds from a transmission designed to withstand 450hp in General Grant tanks.

'Heavy Harry' had a top speed of 55mph, the tractor was driven on the road to its new owners, some 1,200 miles away, over a four-day period at an average speed of 44mph!

Modifying their tractors over the following years the brothers produced a true agricultural tractor in 1969, the Upton 225, powered by a Nissan UD five-cylinder engine rated at 225hp and tank transmissions and drives continued to be used.

The MT Series of Upton tractors was introduced in 1976, initially using a Hercules six-cylinder 200hp engine that was quickly replaced by a Cummins engine rated at 290hp.

The MT designation stood for Medium Tractor; despite their enormous power rating the MT tractors were still two-wheel drive machines. The following year the MT-855 was introduced powered by a V8 Scania engine rated at 300hp.

Field and comparison tests were undertaken on several broadacre farms, the Upton MT-855 proved its worth by easily matching the performance of the American-built four-wheel drive articulated Steiger Panther rated at 310hp.

Carl Upton, after leaving technical college in the late 1960s, became heavily involved with designing the Upton tractors. Each series of tractors was an improvement on the last; along with his brothers he proved that the flat broadacre farms did not require four-wheel drive tractors. As long as the correct ratio of weight to horsepower was maintained a two-wheel drive tractor could out perform a four-wheel drive on the flat land.

By 1978 Carl had built the world's largest production two-wheel drive tractor, the

HT-14/350, a title still held to this day. HT designation for Heavy Tractor, 14 for 14-speed transmission, 350 for 350 engine horsepower.

The HT-14/350, released at the 1978 Ag-Quip show, was Australia's most serious rival for the big four-wheel drives. Until the release of this tractor, the majority of farmers only knew the Upton name for its big boom irrigation systems. Complementing the Upton MT-855 series of two-wheel drives this big tractor put them on the map.

Using identifiable common components such as Cummins engines, Caterpillar axles and Spicer transmissions led to a reliable component-built tractor similar to the majors such as Steiger and Versatile, and the indigenous four-wheel drives. With the

introduction of the HT-14/350 Carl Upton took the concept of two-wheel drive power into another age.

In 1978 the tractor sold for 70,000 Australian dollars, representing a cost of $200 for each horsepower produced, described at the time as the cheapest power available in Australia for farming.

Ballasted for work, the tractor weighed in at 51,592lb, or 23.03 tons. This meant for each engine horsepower there was 147lb of tractor weight. The industry average at that time was 100-120lb weight for each engine horsepower. The saying that 'weight is needed to pull weight' was definitely the case with the big Upton.

Carl believed up to a point that two-wheel drive traction would be able to do everything and more than a four-wheel drive, the point being 350hp.

At various shows and working days Carl's tractor pulled the same pieces of equipment as the big four-wheel drives, successfully proving his point. He says plenty of weight in the right place was the secret, along with big enough tyres to take the load at acceptable wheel slip – performance that was less than 15% had a higher drawbar efficiency on a straight pull.

Where does that weight come from? Well, from various places throughout the tractor. The rear half of the chassis was constructed from four-inch thick plate, the bare rear chassis weighed six tons, the main front chassis members were constructed from 15x6x1in channel.

The 350-gallon fuel tank was made from one-inch thick plate, and when empty weighed three tons. The swinging drawbar was constructed from 6x4in plate in a four-inch frame, the drawbar weighed 1,500lb or 0.66 tons. The hardened drawbar pin had a diameter of three inches. Weight and strength was built into the tractor throughout. ➡

Pulling a 60ft Copperfield blade plough at 5mph with ease, the Upton HT-14/350 certainly turned heads and proved its worth.

Carl Upton had plans to build a four-wheel drive, the HT-1150, to be powered by a 600hp Cummins engine, but the Australian agricultural economy failed in the early 1980s and the big tractor never got off the drawing board.

The tractor had a unique feature for a modern-day machine, the operator's cab was off-set. Carl Upton says by off-setting the cab, operator visibility was greatly improved. The cab was well insulated from both heat and noise from the engine and transmission.

No silencer was fitted to the tractor; the six-cylinder Cummins turbocharged engine 'cracked out', yet when you sat in the cab very little noise was evident.

The operator's cab was mounted on four rubber mounts, a self-contained modular design unit that was one of the largest on the market. The cab was fully air-conditioned with a stereo sound system, along with many other operator comforts including

a swivelling operator seat with swivelling controls.

The tractor was often worked 24 hours at a time so operator comfort was paramount. The 350-gallon tank could keep the tractor running for several days at a time.

The rear tyres, 33.5x33 20-ply, had a 20 per cent greater circumference than the 30.5x32 more commonly used on the big four-wheel drives. Carl found these earthmover tyres provided a high degree of traction with adequate flexing for agricultural work during extreme drawbar pulls.

A large ground contact area of more than 900 square inches provided adequate flotation, which gave a lower ground pressure than many equal sized four-wheel drives. Eighty per cent of the tractor weight was on the rear wheels; under load nearly 88 per cent of weight was transferred to the rear wheels allowing for minimum wheel slippage.

Several smaller MT-855 tractors were upgraded to the HT-14/350 specifications in the late 1970s, but there was only one true Upton HT-14/350 that was designed to become a production tractor. Due to a downturn in the Australian rural economy of the 1980s Upton tractor production ceased despite plans for a large four-wheel drive articulated tractor.

The Upton HT-1150 would have been powered by a Cummins KTA1150 six-cylinder turbocharged engine rated at 600hp. Upton Engineering remained at Corowa concentrating at what they had become nationally recognised for, irrigation systems.

While filming with DT-Media for the *Big Iron 3* video we visited Australia to film the indigenous tractors and to interview the respective manufacturers. While in New South Wales we learned that the Upton HT-14/350 was in the area.

The opportunity to visit the farm and film the world's largest two-wheel drive tractor was too good to miss. The search was on; it did not take to long for us to locate the 350hp giant.

We were told to head about 100 miles north of a small town called Hay and be prepared for the unexpected. Once out of town we saw nothing, no buildings, no traffic, no people and no giant tractors. The land was totally flat, blue skies and temperatures reaching 100 degrees plus in the shade. We were heading into the bush or the outback, we weren't sure, but wherever we were heading we wondered if we would ever see the big yellow two-wheel drive tractor, or any sort of civilisation.

On we went. We came across a derelict hotel called One Tree, an old staging post from the late 1800s, there was nothing but flat land, blue skies and scrub. This area has been described as the flattest place on earth and the One Tree Hotel was in the centre of it with nothing else to be seen for miles.

We headed west to the Murrumbidgee River, the barren plains, void of trees, were

Technical specification

Built:	1978
Engine:	Cummins NTA855
Cylinders:	6 turbo & aftercooled
Horsepower:	350hp
Transmission:	14 forward, 4 reverse
Rear axle:	65,000lb planetary
Fuel capacity:	350 gallons
Length:	258in
Wheelbase:	154in
Width:	141in
Height:	137in
Weight:	51,592lb (20.3 tons)
Clearance:	19in
Turning circle to centre line:	234in
Tyre sizes:	Front: 18.4x26 12-ply
	Rear: 33.5x33 20-ply (E2 earthmover)

The wide off-set cab gives a clear view down the side of the tractor, especially useful when seeding.

home to a few emu, kangaroo and eagles. In the distance we saw trees, was this our destination or a mirage? In fact it was the Charlesville Station, home to the Cary family, the owners of the world's largest two-wheel drive tractor.

We were greeted at the gate of the station (what we call a farm entrance) and on we went through miles of scrub. Driving through a line of eucalyptus trees there it was, a working farm like an oasis in the middle of the outback. The farmstead on the banks of the Murrumbidgee River was the centre of 23,000 acres of fertile farmland.

Harold Cary farms the station with the help of his three young sons who are still at school, their home is their school as they live too far from a village school. Faced with the worst drought for 100 years with a rainfall last year of just five inches, the Cary family tries to make a living from the parched earth.

In a good year when rainfall can be as high as 28 inches wheat yields can reach three tons to the acre, the dry season saw average yields this last harvest of less than eight hundredweight to the acre with many hundreds of acres of crops failing miserably.

Harold irrigates around 5,000 acres a year with the intention in the very near future of irrigating more than half his 23,000 acres on an annual rotation.

In a dry growing season the land can be flood irrigated at least three times, giving three to four inches of water at each flooding and thereby pushing average wheat crop yields over the two tons to the acre mark.

To work all this ground the family use the Upton HT-14/350 that in season works nearly 24 hours a day. At the moment it pulls a set of 33ft 84-blade Ennor off-set disc harrows.

16-year-old Rowan on the left is the main tractor driver, he is seen with his father Harold. Together they farm 23,000 acres of flat broadacre countryside.

Travelling at a healthy 8mph on average the family work 40 acres an hour.

Harold says that the tractor is capable of pulling an implement three times this width, when they work more of the farm for cotton production then new implements will be purchased to fully match the yellow monster.

The Carys purchased the tractor three years ago. Harold can recall seeing this tractor at various shows when he was a youngster, and when he saw it for sale in a dealer's yard in Deniliquin Road he said to his wife that he had seen it working, proving itself against four-wheel drives and it would make a great plough tractor. The tractor was purchased and put straight to work at Charlesville.

Harold says "The Upton pulls just as easy as a modern four-wheel drive and the kids would prefer to drive the yellow tractor.

With it being such a heavy machine there is no power hop, the tractor surges forward and is quite happy working at 8mph all day. Basically it is cheap horsepower, I have calculated that for every 2,000 acres worked we use $2,000 of diesel which is about half the cost of a modern four-wheel drive."

"Since it arrived on the farm, apart from routine servicing the tractor has never had a spanner on it. We do around 3,000 to 3,500 hours a year on this tractor, which is the main workhorse. I firmly believe there are many years work left in the old girl yet.

"It's easy to work on and if the engine ever does fail we can just lift it out and fit a replacement. Apart from that there is no fear of the four-inch thick steel ever letting us down, Carl Upton knew exactly what he was doing when he designed and built the HT-14/350." ➡

The rear half of the tractor is constructed from four-inch thick steel plate, the swinging drawbar is manufactured from 6x4-inch spring steel weighing 0.66 ton.

Harold Cary said: "The Upton pulls just as easy as a modern four-wheel drive; the kids would prefer to drive the big yellow tractor." ■

Bomb-proof build

Introduced in 1979, the Favorit LS range was Fendt's answer to the competition and offered everything a demanding customer could want, remaining in production until 1993. These six-cylinder workhorses are still considered to be a good investment, so Howard Sherren investigates what they have to offer.

riginally the Favorit range offered 95-150hp, but by the early Eighties it had been extended, starting with the 95hp 610, followed by the 105hp 611, 120hp 612, 145hp 614, and the range-topping 165hp 615.

To begin with, the range was fitted with the naturally-aspirated MWM D 226-6 six-cylinder engine, with a rated speed of 2,300rpm for the two smaller models and 2,400rpm for the three larger tractors.

All of the engines had a 105mm bore, 120mm stroke and 6,240cc capacity, apart from the smallest 610 model which had 100mm bore, 120mm stroke and a capacity of 5,652cc.

They also had a 222-litre fuel tank mounted above the engine, which was adequate for most tractors of the period. An optional additional fuel tank was available with a capacity of around 80 extra litres. Re-fuelling was a case of stretching across from the steps or by using the optional toolbox, which came in handy as a footstep.

The 614 and 615 models were fitted with a turbocharger, something that Fendt claimed it had spent a long time researching and developing. The Fendt 614 had the best torque increase of 22%, followed by the 615 at a respectable 19%, 612 at 18% and the smaller two with a 17% increase.

Key facts	
Built:	Bavaria, Germany
Engine:	6-cyl MWM TD226B-6
Power:	165hp
Chassis:	Rigid, four-wheel drive
Typical farm:	Large European arable

In 1976 Fendt launched the Favorit 600 Series; a simple and strong design that made the range popular as it evolved through the 1980s and early 1990s.

Changes to the engines and horsepower occurred in 1984 when firstly the 612 was upgraded with a turbo which took its power up by 15hp to 135hp. In 1987 it was upgraded further when it was pushed to 145hp, which was achieved from the use of the TD 226B-6 MWM engine. The same year saw the 610 model dropped from the line-up, the 611 increased to 125hp, the 614 becoming 165hp and the 615 being upgraded to an incredible 185hp.

The MWM engines should be of little concern, as they can clock up high hours with few problems. Early models were badged 'LS', with models from 1983/4 onwards displaying the improved 'LSA' version.

Transmission

The gearbox fitted was a simple synchromesh transmission offering 20 forward and nine reverse gears. There were six gears in three ranges with a creeper, which achieved the 20 forward speeds.

At first a 40kph top speed wasn't available, 30kph was standard on all models, but it wasn't too long before the higher speed was standard, although the two-wheel drive models were still limited to the lower speed.

Fendt used these features to advertise the range, a high road speed gear to cut travelling time and a reduced engine speed when travelling at 25kph.

In the early part of 1988, Fendt introduced the revolutionary 'Duospeed' hydrostatic transmission that was the benchmark for gearbox design. The system comprised of the existing 20/9 gearbox, but with the addition of an infinitely-variable drive gear that became an option on the range.

A swash-plate hydraulic pump was mounted at the very front of the tractor that was driven straight from the engine crankshaft, which powered a hydraulic motor mounted behind the gearbox. This gave four step-less speed changes, which enabled the tractor to accelerate from zero to the highest speed in that given range at any engine rpm.

This design principle of a step-less forward and reverse drive later became what we know today as 'Vario' transmission technology. At the time, its sophistication and incredible price tag put many customers off, thus leading to only a handful of machines being sold in the UK with this type of gearbox.

All tractors were fitted with a 540 and 1,000 rpm power take-off, both available by changing the stub shaft on the pto drive shaft. The power take-off is engaged by its own multi-disc clutch, which means the engine is not subjected to any axial loading. A smooth and gradual engagement is also achieved via the use of the hand-operated clutch.

Clutch

The 'Turbomatik' feature was another revolutionary design that was only offered by a couple of manufacturers at the time. Turbomatik was the name given to a fluid

Specifications

Model	611 LSA	612 LSA	614 LSA	615 LSA
Engine power (hp)	125	145	165	185
Max power @ (rpm)	2,300	2,400		
Max torque @ (rpm)	1,500			
Number of cylinders	6 Turbo			
Displacement (cc)	6,240			
Bore (mm)	105			
Stroke (mm)	120			
Fuel tank capacity (litre)	222			
Transmission	20 forward, 9 reverse			20 x 9 DuoSpeed
Lift capacity (kg)	7,410			
Turning radius 4wd (mm)	5,600	5,900		6,100
Length (mm)	4,707		4,719	
Width (mm)	2,690			
Standard weight (kg)	5,660	5,955	6,270	6,300
Std. tyre size front	14.9 R28	16.9 R28		18.4 R28
Std. tyre size rear	18.4 R38	20.8 R38		20.8 R38
Cab	Luxury			

clutch design, which was fitted to the Favorit range as standard. It consisted of a turbine wheel and pump impeller submerged in oil.

When the tractor is setting off in gear and the rpm increases, oil is forced from the rotating wheel to the impeller causing it to start rotating smoothly and ending up with both at the same speed when fully engaged.

The idea was that it gave a quick and smooth take-up of drive without causing clutch wear. Another positive point was that any gear could be selected; providing

the gear was not too high, the tractor could be held in a stationary position using the handbrake or foot brakes. All that would be needed to pull away was an increase in rpm, much like an automatic car. This meant it was difficult to stall and the tractor was unlikely to roll backwards.

In 1988 the 'Turbomatik E' became standard on the 615, which was a modification to the standard Turbomatik but with an additional torque converter and a lock-up clutch. The torque converter ➡

This 614 LSA is fitted with a 165hp MWM engine and was the second largest in the range.

later machines featured a single lever in a gate to control both. A front linkage option which gave 3,100kg front lift capacity and a 1,000rpm front power take-off was also available.

With the 'Reverse Drive' option, the tractor could become a very useful piece of kit, especially when using a forage harvester for example. However the feature was never popular in the UK due to the design being too unique.

Axles & brakes
The 610 LS and 611 LS models were the only two tractors in the range to be available in two-wheel drive form. Fendt built its own four-wheel drive front axle that used a side-mounted drive shaft.

A 5.8m turning circle was achievable for the 610 and 611, 6.0m for the 612 and 614, with the 615 taking 6.5m to turn, all obtained from a 50-degree steering angle.

Drive to the front axle could be engaged on-the-move using the dry multi-disc clutch. Four-wheel braking was fitted to all four-wheel drive models via a brake disc on the prop-shaft. The front brakes provided 100% better braking performance compared to the tractors with only rear brakes.

An automatic differential lock known as 'Locomatic' was fitted as standard. It was made up of two opposing multi-disc clutches, which were activated by sliding axle bevel gears once a wheel started to slip.

'Alltronic' gave electronic control of both four-wheel drive and differential locks by a three-way twist switch that was an advanced automatic system for its time.

On the rear of the tractor, unusually, drum brakes were fitted – which weren't the most effective. Optional air braking was beneficial and a good investment. An exhaust brake was also fitted to many tractors to slow the machine safely.

Cab
The Favorit cab was originally fitted with only one door to its square, boxy cab in 1976 but, due to demand, within four years it was replaced by a conventional two-door cab. The doors hinged from the 'B' pillar and opened backwards creating easy access to a very spacious 0.8m² floor area.

A heavy-duty rear linkage was fitted to all tractors in the range and from 1984, larger lift cylinders were used which gave the tractors a 7,410kg lifting capacity. This 612 was fitted with a swinging drawbar, as many opted out of the standard pick-up hitch.

converts the engine torque to speed while accelerating and the clutch locks up the engine and gearbox between 1,600-1,900 rpm, creating an efficient transfer of power.

Also a 'Hydro-electronic' control monitors the gearbox input shaft constantly, so if the engine rpm dropped dramatically when climbing a hill for example, it engaged the torque converter to maintain the engine speed. This feature soon became an option on all models in the range.

Unfortunately though, with incorrect use and abuse, the Turbomatik clutch should be investigated before purchase, as worn or damaged clutches could mean big repair bills.

Hydraulics & rear linkage
The Favorit was fitted with two hydraulic gear pumps. The first was a 54 litre per minute pump to feed the linkage and spools, the second; a 40 l/min pump powered the steering.

This was changed in 1984 when a third smaller 21 l/min pump was added to power the steering. The main hydraulic system consisted of two pumps in tandem; firstly a

26 l/min and the second 46 l/min pump were connected to produce 72 l/min, giving a total available of 93 l/min.

The rear linkage gave lifting capacities from 5,600kg on the 610 up to 7,410kg on the 615 until 1984 when all tractors could lift a maximum of 7,410kg through increased hydraulic capacity and bigger lift.

Controlling the linkage was initially via a simple, single up and down lever with a separate draft lever, until an electronic linkage control system (EHR) was introduced in 1983.

An electro-hydraulic automatic lift unit was fitted to just the 615 prior to the EHR which gave improved, accurate control.

The 'Fendt-Tronic' or 'Electro-Hydraulic Power Lift (EHR)' was one of the first electronic hitch control systems on the market, fitted as standard to all tractors after 1983. A digital speed read-out could be obtained from the EHR, which could be used with metering equipment, such as sprayers, to obtain accurate dosages.

Two spools were fitted as standard, with an optional extra two available. Controlled by individual levers at first, the

History

1976	95-150hp Favorit range launched.
1979	Range badged as 'LS'
1983	Electronic Hydraulic Power-Lift (EHR) replaces manual linkage lever.
1988	610 model dropped from range.
1988	Power increased on 614 and 615 models.
1988	'Duospeed' vario speed transmission launched.
1993	Favorit 500C and 800 Series replaces 600 Series.

Later-type mudguards are fitted to this 612 and house the indicator and sidelight assembly. This was moved from the front of the cab in the late 1980s.

Useful contacts

Bruce Hopkins
AGCO dealer
Banbury, Oxon.
01295 680711
www.brucehopkins.co.uk

G&R Pykett Ltd
Fendt dealer
Ilkeston, Derbys.
01159 322438
www.pykett-tractors.co.uk

Noise levels were low at 78dB(A) on later machines, in-line with or lower than many other manufacturers.

The cab used an impressive 4.6m² of glass, which gave a good view of work. Air-conditioning was an optional extra although opening front and rear windows gave good ventilation but increased noise. A fan was fitted as standard, with the ability to direct hot or cold air at the feet, head or windscreen.

The dashboard originally featured an analogue display, until it was updated in 1988 with a modern digital LCD unit. The dashboard also now featured a number of push buttons for various operations, which were clear and practical to use.

Another external and handy Fendt feature was tilting front mudguards giving cab protection when on the road and providing clearance for field work when tilted forward.

As standard, the tractors weighed between 5,505kg for the 610 up to 6,420kg for the 615. Similar to other tractors, such as the Ford TW Series, the Favorit used 'belly' weights, which meant a further 14 weights could be added to the tractor's existing front axle weight.

Driving

To access the cab of a Favorit, the doors open wide at right angles to the tractor and the steps are a good size and ergonomic. Wide wheel arches hinder access slightly, but otherwise it is very good.

An adjustable seat offers good comfort, although the steering wheel has no adjustment. The clutch is fairly heavy compared to other tractors but feels precise, as do the brakes.

After a few turns, the engine fires up with a fair bit of white smoke which clears after a few minutes. The gear levers are located on a slightly-raised part of the right-side console and are easy to reach and feel accurate and exact.

The uptake of drive is very smooth and even though there is no electronic change, the shifting of gears is simple.

The steering lock is not spectacular, but does not affect the tractors' manoeuvrability too much.

The EHR system is mounted on top of the right wing and is comfortable to use. Spool levers next to the seat can be awkward to use with the armrest in place and the dash-mounted hand throttle can be a stretch.

The dashboard is tidy and simple to read with the push buttons being easy to activate. Views are excellent thanks to large glass and thin pillars, and the additional opening front window gives natural cab ventilation. ➡

Inside the cab a simple brown colour scheme greeted the driver. Its square appearance and large windows made a spacious and light working environment.

This 612 LSA was launched with 145hp. The flagship model, the 615 LSA, at first boasted an impressive 165hp but was given a boost to 185hp in 1987.

Overall the tractor is a pleasure to drive with its combination of mechanical gearbox and electronic controls.

Verdict

The Favorit was Fendt's answer to the growing demand for a stronger, more efficient tractor with a design that was basic and simple to use.

Meeting these requirements exactly, the six-cylinder LS/LSA tractors soon strengthened the Fendt reputation, yet sales were hindered by the brand's premium price.

Sharing many of its components and having a very similar design to the IH/Case IH 1455XL, competition was fierce in the 1980s. It was found that the 1455XL was more popular, due to its lower price tag and parts availability.

Many buyers who purchased the Favorit were current users and were buying the tractor for brand name alone. As current day demands for simple, reliable and 'useable' tractors increases, the Fendt Favorit is a must for those who seek German build quality.

If styling isn't important and a practical tractor is, the Favorit's straight lines and bomb-proof build is for you.

Prices can start from around £5,000 for a basic, early 610 leading up to £18,000 or more for one of the last 615 LSA models produced in 1993. ∎

The dash on earlier tractors featured a series of analogue dials and warning lamps.

The tractormeter was clear and easy to read. Speeds were shown in kilometres per hour.

Gear, hitch and spool levers were within easy reach. No electronics were used on early models.

How much?

Model	Year from	Year to	Mechanical parts availability (out of 5)	Bodywork availability (out of 5)	M	1	2	3
611 LS/LSA	1979	1993	4	4	£14,500	£10,500	£7,800	£4,750
615 LS/LSA	1979	1993	4	4	£16,500	£12,000	£8,500	£5,000

Note: M: Mint condition, 1: Excellent condition with no faults, 2: Tidy condition and useable, 3: Rough condition, for restoration or possibly breaking.

Biggest of them all

One of the most powerful tractors in Europe emerges from restoration. Peter D Simpson went to see the finished work.

Very few of the 516 Big Bud tractors built in Havre, Montana, USA were exported. Production had ceased 13 years previously, when, in 2003, the first example to reach the UK arrived at Southampton.

New owner, Mike Scaiffe from Middlesbrough, said: "I had fully restored a Steiger-built Ford FW-30 and was looking for something new. In the way they are engineered these big tractors present an enormous challenge to restore. The FW-30 weighed in at nearly 15 tonnes while this new monster, Big Bud, weighs in at around 27 tonnes."

Mike's friend Peter Simpson brokered the deal with Ron Harmon, builder of Big Bud tractors. He secured a Series 3 Big Bud 525/50, serial number 81121 (CT 35C 30111121). It was the 121st Big Bud, built during 1981.

"I wanted a tractor that was basically complete but needed a full restoration. The 525/50 fitted the bill nicely. It was an ex-EMS (Earth Moving Systems) tractor used for construction and laser land-levelling duties. It was a bit battered and battle scarred, especially the operator cab," explained Mike.

"The engine was in working order, as was the Twin-Disc Power-shift Transmission. Both are easy to get at, the complete power train just slides out on a skid. The whole tractor was basically sound and just needed stripping down, some repair work to the chassis and tin work, re-wiring, re-plumbing of the hydraulics and then repainting in original Big Bud white and red colours.

Part of the deal was fitting the tractor with new Firestone 30.5x32 dual tyres on the 27-inch rims. To have the tyres fitted in the United States cost £3,000 less than UK prices."

The full restoration of the UK's largest and most powerful agricultural tractor was to take a couple of years. Finished in the autumn of 2005, the Big Bud was re-badged as a 650/50, with a revised horsepower rating, on its official launch on 16 February 2006. ➡

The superbly-finished Big Bud 650/50 weighs in at over 27 tonnes.

Key facts

Built:	Montana, USA
Engine:	6-cyl Cummins KTA-19
Power:	650hp
Chassis:	Articulated, four-wheel drive
Typical farm:	Large American arable

The ex-EMS Big Bud 525/50 being loaded at Southampton Docks ready for its journey north.

Restoration

When the tractor arrived at Middlesbrough, Mike test-drove it to check for potential problems before moving it into the workshop for a complete strip down.

The first assemblies to be removed were the operator's cab and tilting bonnet. Out came the massive six-cylinder Cummins engine, Twin-Disc transmission and drop box, all together on a skid unit. An overhead crane was required to lift the remaining main frame so the axles could be removed and the front and rear units split.

To Mike's surprise, each stripped half of the articulating frames weighed nearly six tonnes. As this particular tractor had been used in the earth-moving industry, pulling a scraper pan, many extras components had been fitted. It took Mike a day just to decide which of the assemblies were added extras.

For instance, extra hydraulic hoses and filters were attached to the rear unit to supply increased oil flow to the big scraper pan.

Instead of the standard swinging drawbar, a complex couple hitch had been added. By the end of the day, there was a large pile of surplus parts.

Mike says: "Stripping the tractor down to its bare components was a mammoth task in its own right as everything was so large and heavy. I think it took in excess of 40 hours, before any more detailed work. What a pile of assorted bits and pieces littered the floor. Framework, wheels, axles, engine, transmission and tin work, 27 tonnes of it."

Before putting the axles away, Mike opened up the hub ends where everything appeared to be in good condition with no worn parts or splines, all that was required were new brake shoes and seals.

"The main pivot point between the two joints was the only area to suffer major damage, the enormous bush and bearing just collapsed. After replacing this, all that was left was to start removing the old paintwork in preparation for applying primer before our damp English winter weather decided to add the dreaded surface rust."

The engine

Mike decided he would have the engine refurbished. John Tipper, Customer Service Advisor, Cummins Diesel at Stockton-on-Tees got the project rolling. He said: "My service controller Wayne Percy and I went to Mike's workshop.

"The tractor was in a million parts, and stood in the middle of the workshop was a KTA-1150 six-cylinder engine." This particular engine was ordered on 28 October 1980 and made in the Jamestown engine plant in America on 4 December 1980. The engine configuration was D193029CX02.

The KTA-1150 engine designation means: K - engine series, T – turbocharged, A - after-cooled, 1150 engine size in cubic inches.

When the overhauled engine left Cummins at Stockton it was re-designated as a metric engine, KTA-19. Again K – the engine series, T – single turbocharged, A – after-cooled, 19 – 19-litre capacity. John Tipper continued: "We noticed it was fitted with a block heater and a Sentinel System. We removed those along with other non-useful bits and pieces.

"There was a variety of fuel pipes to change, we also replaced a missing pipe from the intercooler to the fuel pump, which

The front half of the tractor stripped of components and paint, ready for the next stage.

The newly-refurbished engine, transmission and drop box are ready for assembly.

Everything is big; here Mike stands between the front and rear units lining up the centre pin.

Mike stands over six feet tall, which gives an idea as to the size of the bonnet.

Looking more like a tractor, the front end has been painted and the engine fitted.

Note the scale of the assistant to the front section of the Big Bud tractor.

Right and centre: Mike fitted a Hiab arm to the rear of the tractor so the dual wheels can be lifted off the transport truck and fitted to the tractor with minimal effort.

Bottom: An operation of this magnitude requires the skill and assistance of many people. This is the assembled team who assisted at various stages from producing and fitting the decals to electrics, fabrication and mechanical work.

controls the air-to-fuel ratio for low-down power.

"Mike also wanted the engine horsepower checking and lifting to maximum spec. We removed the fuel pump and checked the calibration. Research by Tom Bolton of the Pump Shop into revised settings brought the engine up to full output of close to 650 horsepower.

"The engine was generally in very good condition. The main work was a repair to a water side-plate where we had to replace the gaskets and bolts. The injectors and valves were cleaned and set and a full service of the engine was carried out, replacing all belts and water hoses as well as the thermostats.

Unfortunately, the obsolete alternator was unrepairable. We did some minor work to replace three rocker cover breathers."

Mike contacted Allison with regard to the tractors Twin-Disc TD-92-2610 full power-shift transmission with nine forward and two reverse speeds. Allison told him 'if it ran well just leave it alone', but recommended renewing the wiring, which Mike has done.

Fabrication & painting

The whole tractor was stripped of paint. Both front and rear mudguards were extended to wrap fully over the wheels. New front mudguards tested the fabricator's skills as they are formed from ⅝in steel. New steps to the operator's cab were also made.

The next stage of the restoration was to paint the front unit, fit the front Clark planetary drive axle, engine and transmission, followed by the assembly and painting of the rear bogie.

"I altered the front tilting hood by enclosing the engine and modifying the cab so the door opened in the opposite direction to permit access from my new entry platform." Mike explained.

"Assembly of the tractor was fairly straightforward but because of the size I needed assistance."

As well as Cummins, help came from Auto Electrics Teesside, who handled the auto electrical work. Sign Studios of Middlesbrough took great care to supply accurate decals.

Mike Scaiffe's company, Cleveland Site Safe, fabricates steel secure site sheds and the lifting facilities and specialist equipment were invaluable in the restoration process, together with the skills of the workforce, whose enthusiasm and assistance Mike gratefully acknowledges in achieving the quality of the end result. ∎

Technical specification

Produced:	1980-84
Engine:	Cummins NTA-855-A310
Cylinders:	6 turbocharged/aftercooled
Bore x stroke:	5½in x 6in
Horsepower:	310hp
Rated speed:	2,100rpm
Transmission:	12 forward, 4 reverse
Speed range:	2.6mph – 15.2mph
Hydraulics:	23.6gpm pump, 2,250psi
Weight:	24,400lb (standard)
Tyre sizes:	24.5x32

This 1982 Versatile 895 is coupled to a Krause no-til box seeder. Photo: Peter D Simpson.

Built to last

Scott Lambert takes a look at the Versatile 895 – an over-engineered monster of the prairies.

Versatile started building four-wheel drive, articulated tractors in 1966 and can lay claim to being the first company to mass produce tractors of this type.

Early tractors produced at the company's Canadian factory in Winnipeg were powered by straight-six or V8 petrol engines, typically producing around 100hp and were quick to gain a reputation for reliability and were praised for their rugged build – the perfect advertisement for a fledgling tractor manufacturer.

By the end of the next decade a Versatile tractor powered by a 330hp engine could be purchased, but the 1980s saw the company's tractors range from over 200hp to in excess

of 450hp – with the 895 model, seen here, producing 310hp at the flywheel and 260hp at the power take-off.

Powered by a Cummins NTA-855-A310 six-cylinder diesel engine, the handsome-looking 895 was introduced in 1980 and had more than enough power for the most demanding applications and was widely used across Canada and North America. Farmers liked its never-say-die attitude and the fact that it was easy to look after – most components were easily accessible and routine maintenance was straightforward.

When production of the model ended in 1984, the 895 cost over $110,000. Three years later Versatile was bought by Ford New Holland, with the famous red and yellow livery changing to blue, white and black in 1989. ■

Key facts

Built:	Manitoba, Canada
Engine:	6-cyl Cummins NTA-855-A310
Power:	310hp
Chassis:	Articulated, four-wheel drive
Typical farm:	Large American arable

The Italian stallion

Looking for an easy-to-use and simple tractor, that is reliable and will cover thousands of hours with ease? Then a Fiat 110-90 could be the answer, says Howard Sherren, as he takes a look at one of the later, New Holland-branded models.

Manufactured in the Italian Jesi plant, the Fiat 90 Series has been around for a long time now, thanks to its design. A simple, reliable and lightweight tractor that anyone can drive has always been a popular machine on the market, and the 110-90 is certainly a very good performer.

The no-frills machine was so good that it was painted blue and re-badged as a New Holland and remained a very good seller across the world. The tractor could be considered as one of the basic models you could buy, similar to a Zetor or Belarus.

The 110-90 first became available in the UK in 1985, although production of the smaller models had appeared two years earlier.

Replacing the 980 and 1180 models, the 100-90 and 110-90 were the 'mid-range', six-cylinder model tractors from Fiat. The remarkable point to realise is that the 110-90 was still available to buy from New Holland up until a few years ago.

Key facts

Built:	Ancona, Italy
Engine:	6-cyl Iveco 8065.05
Power:	110hp
Chassis:	Rigid, four-wheel drive
Typical farm:	European arable

Fiat's long-running 110-90 has been a 'love-it' or 'hate-it' tractor since its launch.

Specifications

Engine	Iveco 8065.05
Engine power (hp)	110
Rated speed (rpm)	2,500
Max torque (Nm)	366 @ 1,400rpm
Number of cylinders	6
Displacement (cc)	5,861
Bore (mm)	104
Stroke (mm)	115
Fuel tank capacity (litre)	130
Transmission	20 forward, 4 reverse
Lift capacity (kg)	4,537
Turning radius 4wd (mm)	4,700
Length (mm)	4,320
Wheelbase (mm)	2,540
Standard weight (kg)	4,400
Std. tyre size front	14.9 R24
Std. tyre size rear	18.4 R34
Cab	Comfort/Super Comfort

The cab door swings back 90 degrees to the tractor giving excellent access, but it is somewhat awkward trying to get through the oddly-shaped doorway.

With just under 20 years of production under its belt, the 110-90 has to be one of the longest-running models of recent years, a status also held by the Case IH 1455XL.

There were a few changes apart from the obvious colours and decals, but many of the alterations that did occur happened in the first few years of production, so aim to buy a later machine if possible.

The main improvements included work to the differentials, and the bodywork also gained the useful addition of a galvanised coating to improve paint life.

A true Winner
The 90 Series was very similar to the 80 it replaced, using the same axles and a very similar cab. Many models sold were four-wheel drive, known as DT models and fitted with the Super Wide Comfort cab.

The last tractors to emerge from the production line were often full specification, which doesn't mean a lot when you compare it to the Fiat Winner tractors that replaced the 100-90 and the larger 'high 90' range in 1993. The 110-90 was carried on right through until 2003 alongside and beyond the Winner.

New Holland took the 110-90 and re-badged it in 1998 maintaining the famous Terracotta livery at first before painting it blue in the new millennium. Sadly, sales of basic tractors dropped across Europe, so production of the 110-90 was reduced by the turn of the century.

The increase in technology and a lower requirement for 'simple' tractors meant that the end of the 110-90 came in 2003.

Many operators then opted for a TM 'Classic' model, which gave a basic specification with a larger and more comfortable cab.

Engine
The Fiat 110-90 used the Iveco 8065.05 power unit. This six-cylinder, 5.8-litre engine produced 110 horsepower at 2,500rpm.

The bore was 104mm and the stroke was at 115mm, typical of a 100hp tractor. The torque figures were very impressive at 366Nm at 1,400rpm, which combined with the low weight meant that this high-revving machine gave excellent performance.

The 110-90 was often praised for its outstanding pulling power, and its huge speed range of up to 2,750rpm could be very useful, but a problem when it came to fuel consumption.

Although in normal use it was considered to be quite frugal on juice, but when driven

hard or with the addition of a turbocharger it could really drink fuel. Often turbo kits were fitted by dealers at a cost of around £1,500, which could take power to beyond 130hp, but the fuel consumption and torque characteristics were greatly affected.

It is advisable to check the power of turbocharged models. If you buy one, try to aim for 125hp as it will give better torque and fuel savings, which is useful when the fuel tank is just 130 litres.

The 110-90 also had a very distinctive bark and whistle, which was amplified by the turbo – a characteristic adored by owners and operators.

The engine is, sadly, very noisy when running away at 2,750rpm, so don't expect a quiet ride in the very basic cab.

The engine is pretty much bomb-proof and will do thousands of trouble-free hours, so just carry out your usual checks for servicing etc. ➡

The 12-inch double-plate clutch, however, is prone to wear and tricky to replace, due to the cab being mounted very close to the transmission bell housing.

Two of the bolts are only accessible from inside the cab with a long extension and universal joint through special access holes in the bulkhead. A time-consuming job that inevitably leads to more expense. Expect a clutch to last around 3,000 to 3,500 hours.

Transmission

The gearbox was again an extremely simple design. A 15 forward and three-reverse box was available as standard, or an optional creeper box with 20-forward and four-reverse could be offered in both 30kph and 40kph versions.

With the creeper fitted, speeds as low as 0.3kph could be achieved, and with five ratios below 1kph it was virtually unique in the 1980s.

The gearbox was operated by two gear levers, one lever with five forward and one reverse speeds and the other lever provided up to four ranges. Keeping it simple meant that it was all manual changes and no hydraulic splitters and changes on the move.

Also a point worth noting is that there is no shuttle, which means the tractor must be stationary before being placed in reverse, otherwise a worrying gear-crunching noise will result. Not ideal for loader work, with many direction or gear changes, but it is ideal for those wanting a tractor for any novice to jump on and drive.

Thanks to its lack of hydraulic packs and complicated shifting, the gearbox should last for years if servicing is maintained. There is little to worry about here, but do check for abuse by ensuring all the gears are obtainable when testing.

Rear linkage & power take-off

Linkage lift capacity wasn't bad at 4,537kg (considering the weight and power of the tractor) with one assistor ram fitted as standard. A second ram was often specified by owners if the tractor was likely to be carrying out a lot of ploughing – for example, when it would be on its limits with a heavy four-furrow. It's worth looking out for the extra assistor ram if the tractor is to be bought for arable operations. The linkage drop arms were well protected and the lower links were fairly robust and could stand a lot of abuse.

The tractors were fitted with an Axla pick-up hitch as standard. Some dealers and operators replaced this with a more robust Dromone version – ideal for those who were intending to do more road work.

If the hitch is bent or damaged, expect to pay around £800 for a complete new fit.

The linkage was controlled by position and draft levers combined with a 'click clack' device called 'Lift-O-Matic' for a quick raising and lowering of the implement. This could be stiff to operate and very hard work on your thumb after a day's ploughing: not the best design!

Be warned that the system can come out of adjustment as the cable stretches, thus making the arms drop slowly, though adjustment is an easy-to-rectify problem.

The power take-off offered 540rpm and 1,000rpm speeds, thanks to three bolts and an exchangeable shaft. 540rpm was available at just 2,100 engine rpm, and 1,000 was achievable at 2,400 engine rpm. The engine supplies 100 per cent of its power to the power take-off at 1,000rpm, ideal for work such as big baling.

A synchronised ground speed drive is standard, which can be very useful, and a wide stroke lever provides a smooth engagement. Look out for abused linkages and try to assess the condition of the 12-inch clutch.

Hydraulics

Unfortunately, hydraulic power wasn't particularly high at just 44-45 litres per minute, although a 55-57 litre/min pump was available as an option and standard on later machines. If hydraulics will be used to power motors and various demanding hydraulic systems, it would be advisable to avoid the 110-90. On the plus side the replacement hydraulic pump is relatively inexpensive.

The open-centre hydraulic system operated at 190 bar and featured a paper element filter on the suction side. Up to three spools could be specified and two were standard. The spool valve linkage ball joints often pop off under the cab which is a nuisance rather than a major problem.

Axles & brakes

The front axle received many changes over the years and it pays to go for a post-1989 model.

After this date, the axle was fitted with twin rams to improve the manoeuvrability, as this enabled Fiat to increase the castor angle effect. The steering angle of 50 degrees produced a turning circle of 4.7m, good for a 100hp machine. ➡

New Holland dropped the Fiat name for its own decal in the late 1990s, but very few other changes figured in the tractor's production.

Watch out for leaking axle seals.

Fiat's long-running 110-90 has been a 'love-it' or 'hate-it' tractor since its launch.

Multi-disc brakes on the front differential assisted with braking when both pedals were pressed together. Robust epicyclic gears in the final drive were well engineered and the wet disc brakes slowed the tractor effectively.

Watch out for leaking axle seals both on the front and rear of the tractor.

Cab

The 110-90 came with two cab options: the basic 'Comfort' cab or full-specification 'Super-Comfort' version. Both were actually very basic and had a box-like design. The cheaper 'Comfort' cab had no air-conditioning and poor heaters, but did have the advantage of narrow pillars to improve visibility. But many tractors were specified with the 'Super-Comfort' model, which later became standard.

Two thin steps lead up into the cab, which are easily knocked. The doors on were hinged from the rear and folded out 90 degrees to the tractor to improve access. The slanted door aperture means squeezing into the seat is tricky.

Long-legged drivers will not appreciate the cab, as seat movement was limited and there was only a small amount of space between the seat and the front of the cab.

When seated it feels that the driver is very much 'in' the tractor, sandwiched between the protruding fenders, with not much space for the tool kit or lunch bag.

A mechanical seat will be fitted to many tractors as a cheaper alternative to a worn-out air-seat, but Grammar air seats should be standard on all later machines. Seat coverings were certainly not up to the job

No fancy electronic gauges here! A completely analogue dashboard won't complicate matters on this very simple machine.

The hand throttle was basic and the gear knobs had a tendency to break off in your hand.

Useful contacts

Bennett Tractor Sales
Bandon, Co. Cork, Ireland
023-46133
www.bennetttractorsales.com

C & O Tractors
Blandford, Dorset
Tel: 01258 451221
www.candotractors.co.uk

Ernest Doe
Ulting, Essex
Tel: 01245 380311
www.ernestdoe.co.uk

Farm Services
Elgin, Scotland
Tel: 01343 541121
www.farmservices.co.uk

G & J Peck Ltd
Ramsey St Mary's, Cambridgeshire
01733 844642
www.peck.co.uk

Russells
Kirkbymoorside, Yorkshire
01751 431381
www.russells.uk.com

Lift capacity was 4,537kg, but an extra assistor ram can be fitted to increase capability.

and the upholstery is likely to be torn on most models.

Visibility wasn't spectacular, though the flat glass was easy to replace if it was ever broken.

The dashboard was fully analogue, no fancy electronics anywhere to be seen, keeping it simple! Gear levers were to hand by the driver's right knee and you couldn't go wrong with the large hand-throttle lever mounted to the right mudguard.

Large removable side panels were a bit awkward to remove, but once off, the engine

To the driver's left, the four-wheel drive, parking brake and pick-up hitch levers.

was very accessible. Paint work shouldn't be a worry since Fiat began Zinc coating in the late 1990s, so even if the paint was chipped or scratched off, the galvanised metalwork underneath is unlikely to rust.

Verdict

The 'no-frills' New Holland Fiat 110-90 is a 'love-it' or 'hate-it' affair for many potential buyers.

The simplistic and bomb-proof design which anyone can drive could be well suited to your requirements. On the other hand, someone wanting something comfortable and operator friendly could be advised to look elsewhere.

The 110-90 is certainly a tractor designed to work many hours with very little problems, with the bonus of cheap replacement parts.

A lively engine, teamed with a completely manual gearbox means that power is not lost and you can get all the horsepower to the ground. Always budget for a replacement clutch when looking at a second-hand buy and a new seat will often be required.

It is difficult to put a price on these tractors, due to the range having been through two decades of production. In fact, they hold their money surprisingly well.

Tractors will start at around the £5,000 mark for an early model, with many mid-1990s' versions around the £12,000 mark – with some of the last low-houred blue models fetching up to £20,000.

Export demand is extremely high, with many tractors heading to the Republic of Ireland and across to mainland Europe, so be quick if you see one. ■

How much?

Model	Year from	Year to	N	1	2	3
110-90	1985	2003	£35,000	£20,000	£12,000	£5,000

Note: N: Last new price, 1: Excellent condition with no faults, 2: Tidy condition and useable, 3: Rough condition, for restoration or possibly breaking.

Force II be reckoned with

The Ford TW Series started life in 1979, when the American-built 8700 and 9700 were introduced to the United Kingdom. Howard Sherren takes a look at the darker blue Force II tractors, which arrived in 1986 with a host of improvements.

The development of four-wheel drive and high-powered tractors took place during the 1970s for Ford when they needed a new high-horsepower range to compete with the other leading manufacturers.

So Ford looked at ways of getting more power out of the 6.6-litre engine as fitted to the 8700 and 9700, which were in current production. It had already gone as far as possible with turbo-charging engines, so the next step would be to try air-cooling.

This design used an intercooler, fitted in conjunction with the turbo to cool the air before it entered the cylinders. Cooler air has greater density and because of this, a larger volume of fuel can be burnt in the correct air-to-fuel ratio, and therefore give an increase in power.

Three TW models where brought in to update the 8700 & 9700, and they incorporated many of the engine improvements which were made to the intercooled engine.

The tractors had revised gearbox ratios, which gave a slightly higher speed to reduce torque loading on the Dual Power and other driveline components. Dual Power itself, rear axle, differential lock, and independent power take-off components were also revised and strengthened. The electrical system also received improvements.

The styling of the new tractors was similar to the 8700 & 9700, but the TW-30 had an extended bonnet, which housed a large 78-gallon fuel tank.

Key facts

Built:	Antwerp, Belgium
Engine:	6-cyl Ford 6.6 litre
Power:	170hp
Chassis:	Rigid, four-wheel drive
Typical farm:	Large European arable

Left: The TW-15 is instantly recognisable by its shorter bonnet.

Prices originally started at £15,932 for a two-wheel drive Ford TW-10, rising to £24,905 for a four-wheel drive TW-30.

In 1983, a new phase of TWs were introduced, again at the SIMA show in Paris. The new models were the TW-15, 25 and 35. They had similar looks and features; however they received re-powered engines and other improvements.

The TW-15 and TW-25 both used the same engine as on the previous TW-20 model, with the fuel pump de-rated on the TW-15 to 143bhp and recalibrated on the TW-25 to give 163bhp. The TW-35's fuel system was also tweaked to boost output to 195bhp, 11 per cent more power was claimed by Ford for the new TW Series engines and among the lowest rated engine speeds for this horsepower in agriculture.

Towards the end of 1985, Ford launched the "Force II" TW tractors which featured a new colour scheme and cab design. The same 15, 25 and 35 models where retained. The tractors received a slightly darker blue paint scheme for which New Holland is recognised today.

General tractor design was unchanged. The old Q cab received improvements including a newly-designed roof with added halogen work lights, improved ventilation and simplified access to the filter. The new ➡

Launched on 4 March 1979 at the SIMA show in Paris, the new TW tractors gathered a lot of interest among large farmers and

The TW Series was headed by the 186hp TW-35 which was a popular choice on arable farms until it was replaced by the Powershift 30 Series.

contractors. The TW range consisted of three models, the 128bhp TW-10, 153bhp TW-20 and the 188bhp TW-30.

The main production centre for the TW range was Antwerp, Belgium. It produced models for Britain, Europe and most of the export markets, but manufacturing also took place in Romeo, Michigan, mainly in two-wheel drive form for the North American market.

Specifications

Model	TW-15	TW-25	TW-35
Engine power (hp)	132	154	186
PTO power (hp)	121	141	170
Rated speed @ (rpm)		2,200	
Max torque (Nm)	511	550	617
Number of cylinders		6T	
Displacement (cc)		6,600	
Bore (mm)		112	
Stroke (mm)		112	
Cooling	Naturally aspirated	Oil cooler	Air-to-air intercooler
Fuel tank capacity (litre)	220	378	
Transmission	Dual Power 16 forward, 4 reverse		
Lift capacity (kg)		6,800	
Turning radius 4wd (mm)	5,110	5,390	
Length (mm)	4,586	4,861	
Width (mm)	2,089		2,150
Standard weight (kg)	6,450	6,740	7,120
Std. tyre size front	14.9 R28		16.9 R28
Std. tyre size rear	18.4 R38		20.8 R38
Cab	Super Q		

Engines are usually pretty reliable but can go porous, so check for milky oil.

design was named the "Super Q". The height of the cab was reduced by 75mm and a roof hatch was added. Inside, a new electronic dash replaced the old, dated version with an electronic instrument panel; a performance monitor was available at extra cost and transferred information such as wheel slip and acres covered.

Cab controls, seat and panels all received the new black and blue colour. Noise levels had been reduced to 78dBA for operator comfort and hydraulic and power take-off levers received colour coding for easier use.

Engine design and output remained the same but it now came with a 2,000-hour, two-year warranty. This showed the confidence Ford had in its engines.

The 16x4 Dual Power transmission remained but improvements where made to the Dual Power clutches to make the shifts smoother. A new 32 litre/min auxiliary hydraulic pump gave increased flow capacity on four-wheel drive models and lift capacity was also raised to give 6,860kg.

New deluxe remote control valves gave four setting positions of raise, neutral, lower and float. The cosmetic changes made included, distinctive new bonnet decals and the Super Q cab design. The exhaust fitted to the new TW-15 replaced the dated 'rain cap' look as on the older model.

New front axles where fitted on all models; the TW-15 received a ZF APL 355, with the TW-25 and 35 receiving the stronger APL 356 version to take the extra stress posed on them by the larger fuel tank and extra front weights.

Although Ford introduced a "Generation III" range of tractors for the 10 Series in 1989, the TW range did not obtain this further upgrade. Instead, the 30 Series was born in 1990, which featured the biggest development yet. Another three models using the same engines and cabs but featured an 18-speed Funk power-shift gearbox.

These were produced until 1994 when Ford launched the all-new 70 Series. These newer models had considerably more

electronics on them and are considered not as 'rugged' as the faithful TWs. Powerful, high-torque engines, mated to a simple gearbox and hydraulic system, make the TWs trustworthy and reliable workhorses that will still out-perform many modern-day machines with their high work rates.

Engine
All tractors used Ford's proven 'big bore – short-stroke' 6.6 litre (6,572cc), 6-cylinder engine with a turbocharger and under-piston cooling. The smallest of the range, the TW-15 provided 132 horsepower and 511Nm of torque at 1,600rpm, not bad for a compact machine.

Next along the line was the TW-25 at 154hp and 550Nm of torque, whilst the flagship TW-35 boasted 186hp and 680Nm again at 1,600rpm. The bore was equal to the stroke at 112mm, an unusual design compared to other manufacturers.

The original TW-30 and later 35 were intercooled to give greater output and were also the first agricultural tractor to feature

the "air-to-air" design. It also had an oil cooler mounted on the side of the engine, another different design.

The TW-15 only had a 223-litre fuel tank, but with the longer bonnets, the TW-25 and TW-35 could hold a whopping 379 litres.

Sadly there was a negative to this; the fuel filler cap was located in the centre of the bonnet, a very awkward position for re-fuelling – a process which sometimes resulted in diesel being spilt across it and the paint peeling off.

The huge exhaust stack in the centre of the bonnet also hindered forward visibility. Sadly at the turn of the century the TW and later 30 Series was classed as obsolete and many parts became not so readily available. These could only be ordered from the United States.

Check for the usual Ford problems such as water in the oil where the engine would become porous. Make sure it runs smoothly, no excessive smoke or breathing.

When shutting the tractor off listen out for the intercooler fan winding down on the TW-35. If you can hear this noise, the shaft bearings will probably need replacing – this is before they catch the housing, leading to more damage. In general though, the engine is trouble-free.

Transmission
The transmission found in the TW was a 16-forward by 4-reverse Dual Power unit, known as the "crash box". It was awkward to use during both field and road use, though it rarely gave any problems and as time has proved, it was very reliable.

The Dual Power system incorporated a rugged planetary gearset located directly behind the clutch in the bell housing. An electrically-controlled hydraulic clutch was operated via a foot switch located on the cab floor.

Once depressed, groundspeed was reduced by 22 per cent and torque increased by 28 per cent. It also doubled all available gear ratios.

Lots of smoke, oil from the breather and difficult starting may indicate that the engine is worn and it requires a rebuild.

Left: The Dual Power gearbox featured the traditional two levers and foot-operated DP switch to give 16 forward and 4 reverse gears.

gave outstanding reliability, and remained virtually unchanged throughout its existence.

Top speed was sadly only 30kph, and 40kph wasn't introduced until the Powershift 30 Series. Check that the Dual Power changes up and down smoothly, there is rarely a problem here but some abused models may give issues.

Rear linkage & power take-off

With a lift capacity of 6,860kg, the TW Series was certainly up to the job of lifting the heaviest of arable machinery and twin assistor rams were fitted to all models which boosted the lift by 46 per cent to this new level.

The principle of the design was similar to that of rival Multi-Power, Torque Amplifier, and Power Synchron systems from other manufacturers, yet Ford's Dual Power

With two sturdy drop arms and beefy lower link arms, the tractors could be hooked to a large mounted plough without too many issues. Category II was standard while Category III could be specified as an option on the TW-35.

A swinging drawbar was standard, so look out for models fitted with an optional Ford or ARM pick-up hitch if you are looking to use the tractor for trailer work.

Depth control was chosen using a sturdy lever, while draft was controlled by a smaller lever to the rear of the side console, again idiot-proof. If the tractor was used excessively on three point-linkage work, the cross shaft and bushes in the centre casing wore, which caused the o-ring either side of the casing to leak.

To cure this was a big job, with the top cover off and a wheel removed to slide the shaft out. Check for the usual play or damage in pivots if heavy implements have been involved.

A two-speed 540/1,000rpm power take-off and self-adjusting, single-disc brakes were standard on the smaller TW-15 and ➡

Long protruding bonnet hides the heavyweight Ford 6.6-litre engine on the larger TW-25 and 35; the TW-35 also features an intercooler.

Three wide steps lead up to a tight cab door frame onto the almost flat floor. Corrosion around the cab frame was a common occurrence, so check the seriousness of the situation.

TW-25. The TW-35 was less versatile as it only had a single 1,000-rpm pto, but it wasn't a major requirement of a tractor of this size.

The pto clutch pack is a problem on machines doing heavy pto work. The unit is not strong enough and the friction plates can burn out making the unit slip. Also the pto brake, which is a metal disc running around the clutch drum, can wear into the drum and break up.

To repair the latter is a considerable undertaking, which involves cab removal, splitting the tractor at the trans/rear axle buckle-up joint and removing the pto unit.

Hydraulics

Two different, separate pumps powered the hydraulic system on the original TW range. The TW-15 and TW-25 used a Plessey high-pressure gear-type pump which provided oil to the three-point linkage – whereas a more powerful Webster pump was used on the TW-35.

The second was a low-pressure pump that operated the Dual Power clutches, differential lock, independent pto clutch and lubricated the driveline components. The power brakes on the TW-35 were also operated by this second pump.

The system remained relatively unchanged right through until the 30 Series, which provided 108 litres per minute at rated speed and at a maximum pressure of 2,500psi.

A 32 litre/min auxiliary pump provided flow and capacity to four remote valves. Through years of development, the hydraulics are a pretty reliable area, though check the quick-release spool valves for leaks. (A repair kit is a relatively small expense.)

It should be noted that the cab sits low on these tractors and clearance between it and the transmission is small. This makes it difficult to work on the large-diameter ridged hydraulic lines that can fracture

and leak or need tightening etc. and also increases noise in the cab.

Axles & brakes

The TW tractors used ZF front axles. With the four-wheel drive engaged, the turning radius for the ZF was just 5.39m (4.93m disengaged) on the TW-25 and TW-35 – very good considering the size of the tractor, and the TW-15 was even less at 4.65m and 5.1m.

The 6.8-ton lift capacity was thanks to two assistor rams fitted as standard.

How much?

Model	Year from	Year to	N	1	2	3
TW-15 II	1986	1989	£36,284	£9,500	£6,250	£2,750
TW-25 II	1986	1989	£38,600	£10,500	£7,000	£3,250
TW-35 II	1986	1989	£43,600	£11,000	£8,000	£4,000

Note: N: Last new price, 1: Excellent condition with no faults, 2: Tidy condition and useable, 3: Rough condition, for restoration or possibly breaking.

An array of levers can be confusing to start with, but they are simple and fall easily to hand.

Useful contacts

Bowland Tractors
Winsford, Cheshire
01606 863414
www.bowland-tractors.co.uk

C & O Tractors
Blandford, Dorset
Tel: 01258 451221
www.candotractors.co.uk

Ernest Doe and Sons
Ulting, Essex
Tel: 01245 380311
www.ernestdoe.co.uk

Farm Services
Elgin, Scotland
Tel: 01343 541121
www.farmservices.co.uk

Russells
Kirkbymoorside, Yorkshire
01751 431381
www.russells.uk.com

Robert Wraight Ltd
Ashford, Kent
01233 622985
www.robertwraightltd.co.uk

Watch out for front axle pinion bearing and seal failure, also trunnion pins and bushes wear if not greased and, once missed, soon become blocked and can only be cleared by removing casting and pushing out the blockage.

The front axle in some situations could not handle the power and weight of the TW-35, so check the oils and listen for nasty noises coming from here. Induction-hardened axles, new stronger alloys and larger oil coolers all help to improve the reliability of the rear end. Large oil-immersed disc brakes provide an effective and reliable braking system, and trailer brakes also help to stop safely.

Check the four-wheel drive engages/disengages and that the brakes provide effective stopping power.

Cab

The legendary SQ cab was loved by many Ford fans. Providing noise levels as low as 80dBa, the Super 'Q' cab provided a good environment in which to work, although it wasn't the most spacious on the market.

The first TW cab was designed and built by GKN Sankey, and at the start gave a low noise level of just 83dBA. The interior was made to last. Through many years of use the later 30 Series was likely to be the best thanks to all the development of the range.

Steps were kept clean thanks to their wide gap and it was a comfortable jump up. Ford used a Grammar air seat with a very practical black-with-blue-stripe upholstery. This gave a firm yet comfortable ride, but the front of the cushion would often be worn through

due to the relatively thin covering. The predominant dash housing wasn't too bad, but made it quite a narrow gap for getting to the seat.

Once the driver was seated, the cab pillars were average and hindered visibility, as did the huge exhaust silencer rising from the top of the bonnet. The dashboard had a large LCD digital display on later models providing figures and a series of bars for fuel and temperature etc.

The analogue hour gauge in the centre of the dashboard only had four figures, so once it reached 9,999 hours it was reset, so bear this in mind when looking at a possible high-houred machine.

The electronic dash was very reliable and any problems that do occur will likely be in the wiring department, but it can be fixed if does turn out to be more serious. The side console was neat and tidy with all the simple levers to hand, while the power-shift lever and its display were excellent.

One of the major concerns for this cab was rust and rot, so check all round the doors and windscreen for signs of serious corrosion. Also check that the air-conditioning system is not on R12 gas, as

converting it to R134a will be another large expense in the future.

Verdict

The TW range would not make the best purchase for a mainline tractor, but if you need a reliable, old lugging tractor, it could be the tractor for you.

Engines aren't trouble free but with careful checks of the oil, bad ones can be spotted. Coming standard with belly weights and often fitted with wheel and front weights, the sheer weight of these machines helps to increase traction.

There are still plenty around to look over, but many are now being snapped up by collectors and enthusiasts, which is bumping the price up. There are also a few firms importing them into Britain from France and Germany increasing numbers, but look out for pick-up hitches on British models. Though importantly, if checked over thoroughly there shouldn't be anything to surprise the buyer, making them a cheap, dependable buy.

Expect to pay around £7,000 to £10,000 for a tidy example, with models starting as low as £5,000. ■

Digital dash first appeared in Super Q cab-equipped tractors and is pretty much trouble free.

Caterpillars on rubber

Paul Tofield tells the story of the $100,000 Challenger.

It is more than 20 years since Caterpillar launched the Challenger 65 rubber-tracked agricultural tractor, but although production did not begin until 1986, the concept was being developed in the mid-1970s.

At that time Caterpillar's product line was led by construction and mining machines, apart from a range of agricultural crawlers which were popular in the USA but had no significant impact in world markets which had moved on to rubber-tyred tractors.

But the world market for heavy construction equipment became saturated and more competitive as European and Japanese companies entered the mature

and, in some cases, declining market – so Caterpillar looked for new products.

The company was to become successful in the volume backhoe loader market as a latecomer where a 'me too' product would not be good enough. The backhoe loaders were launched in the mid-1980s as 'better than' products.

Caterpillar also wanted to re-establish a position in the agricultural tractor market and, as the backhoes were being developed, Caterpillar Vehicle Engineering began work on a rubber-tyred, articulated, four-wheel-drive tractor.

The concept was to use existing expertise from the pivot steer wheel loaders and by 1979 a prototype was field tested. The design had problems and was deemed too

expensive to manufacture so a revised and much-improved second tractor appeared in 1981.

From 1979, another group investigated the possibilities of a rubber-tracked crawler as opposed to an articulated four-wheel drive conventional tractor.

At the time one project involved a much-modified D4E SA tractor with a D3306 diesel of 240hp mated to a Fuller truck transmission, which was used to test various powertrain combinations.

Concurrently a series of trials of rubber tracks on a test rig based on the drive system of a Caterpillar 130 grader were undertaken.

The marriage of the powertrain work and rubber track tests produced a belted agricultural tractor which showed more

The Caterpillar Challenger 65 was a radical new concept in high-horsepower agricultural tractors when announced in 1986. The 270 flywheel horsepower tractor weighs over 13 tonnes yet still only has a six pound per square in ground pressure.

Left: The first Caterpillar Challenger 65 sold in the United Kingdom went to a farm in Suffolk in September 1988.

potential than the articulated wheeled-tractor project so the rubber track and wheeled-tractor teams merged into a single group to construct a viable rubber-tracked agricultural crawler.

In 1983 a pair of D6D SA steel-tracked tractors were modified to test the undercarriage combination of rubber-belted tracks driven by friction from rear wheels using two-inch thick solid-rubber drive tyres bonded to the rim of the drive wheels.

The front idlers were pneumatic tyres and the bottom weight-carrying rollers were miniature versions of the rear drive wheels. Four weight-carrying rollers were used. The front and rear pairs were attached to Y-shaped yokes which, in turn, were connected to a main bogie assembly that could pivot.

The bogie suspension was provided by an air bag acting as a spring. This was essentially the Mobil-trac system MTS fitted to the Challenger 65. The Mobil-trac was an endless rubber belt containing four layers of flexible steel cables able to resist the high-tensile loads required for successful friction drive.

Rubber-belted tracks with steel cables embedded had been tried by the US military 40 years earlier on Weasel light carriers. The belts had steel track plates riveted on and used an open-framed steel sprocket drive.

Some post-war small crawlers were also offered with endless rubber tracks.

Extensive testing on the company proving grounds and in the field with a pair of converted D6D SA tractors paved the way for the construction of the first real Challenger unit in February 1984. Then pre-production units followed for testing during 1985 when they were placed with users in the USA. In late 1986, the Challenger 65 was officially launched by Caterpillar with commercial production units becoming available in early 1987.

Caterpillar could now claim that this was the first high-power agricultural tractor designed with a rubber-belted track and undercarriage for sustained high drawbar pulls.

The American Society of Agricultural Engineers gave Mobil-trac its Concept of the Year award in 1987, but it was not all smiles at Caterpillar as the early Challenger 65s began to show drive reliability problems. The company acted quickly to modify the tractors after slippage of the drive belts on the rubber rims was found on downhill braking. Track tension was increased from 10,000lbs to 17,000lbs.

The extra stresses on the drive train bearings and housings and the undercarriage components meant much of the drive and undercarriage had to be upgraded. Unofficial estimates have suggested that it cost Caterpillar $30,000 per tractor to overcome the drive system issues.

With the Challenger 65, Caterpillar could offer a tractor with many totally new features and it was a leap forward in the technology applied to agricultural workhorses rather than an evolution of an existing product. ➡

Key facts

Built:	Minnesota, USA
Engine:	6-cyl Caterpillar 3306 DITA
Power:	270hp
Chassis:	Rigid, rubber-tracked crawler
Typical farm:	Large arable

A Knight Triple Press 700 with a 6.6-metre working width breaks down ploughed land behind a Caterpillar Challenger 75.

In his opening remarks in *Caterpillar World* magazine under the heading 'Why Agriculture Now?' in 1987, Caterpillar executive vice-president Don Fites likened the launch of Challenger to the arrival of the Holt and Best track-type tractors some 80 years earlier.

Caterpillar believed that although farming was undergoing painful change at the time the new Challenger would allow its users to cut costs, increase productivity and benefit from economies of scale.

There was nothing like Challenger in the marketplace, it had no direct competitor, and the target buyers tended to have a conservative view of radically new technology. Embracing the wrong farming system would destroy a farm business already operating on very slim margins.

Not only did Caterpillar need to sell Challenger as a premium price product, it also had to sell the concept of Mobil-trac and its long-term economic justifications through a dealer network which contained few distributors whose core sales were in agriculture.

Only ten per cent of Caterpillar's annual unit sales were agricultural. Dealers and sales staff, as well as farmers, had the Challenger sold to them. A 'sales literature offensive' explained the Mobil-trac concept, describing features and benefits, including some as question and answer to counter customer objections, alongside the normal product brochures.

The Mobil-trac system was promoted on reduced wheel slippage, reduced compaction from high contact area with the land and ability to travel on hard roads at up to 18mph. Tests at maximum drawbar

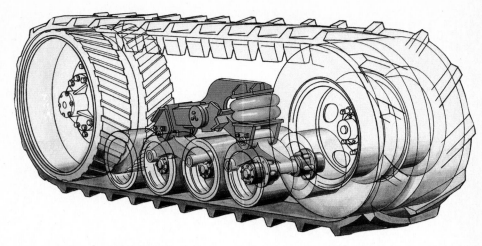

The Caterpillar Mobil-trac system in its early form used a pneumatic front wheel, and steel rear driving wheel. A rubber friction surface was bonded to the drive wheel to grip the track belt which contained four flexible steel cables. The four small wheels are carried on minor bogies (in blue) which in turn are attached to the major bogie (shown in red). The four track rollers are cushioned by air suspension (yellow).

power had shown slippage of four per cent with the rubber track against 15 per cent with a similar four-wheel-drive tractor. Cat estimated that track life was about one and a half times that of tyres. The ground pressure of a 13½-tonne Challenger 65 would be 6psi, which was about half that of an equivalent articulated four-wheel-drive tractor.

The first Challenger 65 sold in the UK was in September 1988 to a 3,000-acre farm in Suffolk. It was worked hard night and day during busy times on heavy-draft work through two drier-than-average summers. The machine was re-tracked at just under 2,400 hours. Wheeled tractors under normal conditions required tyres at around 2,000 hours.

When launched in the USA, the Challenger 65 carried a price tag of a neatly-rounded $100,000, equating to about £65,000. For comparison in the UK, a Ford TW-35 was listed at £42,000 and a Caterpillar D6D SA VHP retailed at £66,400 in July 1987.

Parting with $100,000 for a Challenger 65, the buyer could drive away a 13.5-tonne tractor powered by a Caterpillar 3306 direct-injection turbocharged and aftercooled engine developing a gross 270hp at 2,100rpm from its 10.5 litres.

The transmission was a full power-shift unit with on-the-go shifting in ten forward speeds and two reverse. Six of the ten forward speeds were in the 4 to 7mph speed range for tillage work.

A Challenger 65 at work with a set of Simba heavy discs.

Left: The 75C was matched to a Dowdeswell eleven-furrow plough when demonstrated at the British Ploughing Championships held near Daventry in 1998.

Caterpillar decided against clutch and brake steering, in which full engine power can be transmitted to one track, opting for differential steering which allowed engine power to both tracks during a turn.

A steering wheel operated the differential via a hydraulic pump and motor, the hydraulic steering motor driving the steering differential to speed up one track and slow down the other. This differential steering system was also incorporated in the new D8N dozer.

The jewel in the crown of the Challenger was Mobil-trac, which gave the tractor the mobility of a wheeled tractor with the extra field performance offered by the contact length of rubber tracks. In 1990 the Mobil-trac system on the 65 was awarded a Royal Agricultural Society of England Gold Medal.

The ROPS cab was air-conditioned with a sound level of 77.5dB(A). The cab and nose styling owed much to the prototype articulated wheeled tractors.

Caterpillar also built a steel-track crawler based on a D6D, known as the AG6. This machine was designed for drawbar work and lacked a three-point linkage. The 3306 diesel was set to deliver 200hp when first or second gear was selected and 240hp in gears three to six. The cab and styling again were similar to the Challenger. Although production ran from 1986 to 1993, only around 30 AG6 tractors were built. It is believed two of these reached the UK.

Early sales of the Challenger were slow as potential buyers were unsure if this tractor was just a one-off wonder, but it was a clear indication that the concept was sound enough to attract competitor products when John Deere entered the market with the 8000T Series rubber-tracked crawler in 1996 and Case IH launched the Quadtrac 9370 in 1997.

Caterpillar filed a lawsuit against John Deere for patent infringement following the launch of the 8000T Series. Maybe there is no such entity as bad publicity as sales of the Challenger row-crops and standard Challengers increased with the advent of competitive tractors.

During the ten years it took the opposition tractors to reach commercial production, the Challenger 65, with its equal-sized drive and front idler wheels, had now reached Series E making it the smallest member of a family of four now being joined by the 75E, 85E and 95E. The C to E Series Challengers had a fixed track gauge of 90 inches and a range of different track belt widths was offered; the original 65 gauge was 84.7 inches.

In 1994 a second line of Challengers, suitable for row crops and using a large drive wheel, small diameter front idler and three track rollers was introduced. The Challenger 35, 45 and 55 tractors featured an undercarriage which could be set for a number of different widths and be fitted with narrow belts for row crop work.

It was possible to order the earlier models with a fixed track gauge, but the majority of the tractors were able to have the track gauge varied between 80 and 120 inches, using spacers. Seven spacers from one inch to 20 inches were available. Two base tractor track gauges of 60 and 80 inches were shown in the 1997 specifications.

The launch of the Challenger 35 and 45 had been planned for 1992. Since these tractors were being built with a Fiat/Ford Genesis back end in what was the old Versatile factory in Winnipeg, issues with the new Genesis tractor range delayed the launch of the row-crop Challengers until 1994 in the UK. Production of the row-crop models was relocated to the DeKalb site in October 1998 as a prelude to manufacture of prototypes for the new MT Series.

Unlike their larger counterparts, which used a Caterpillar-designed and built ten-forward and two-reverse speed power-shift transmission, the 35, 45 and 55 Challengers used a Funk power-shift with 16 forward and nine reverse speeds. A 1,000-rpm power take-off and rear three-point hitch were fitted as standard. On the large Challenger family the power take-off and hitch were listed as options.

In August 1997, Cat Claas Europe was formed to sell the 35, 45 and 55 along with the Challenger E Series range. The change from Caterpillar yellow to Claas green and white may have upset a few purists, but sales grew well – proving that it was the concept that was a winner, not just the Caterpillar name on the bonnet. ■

A 200hp Challenger 45 drills spring barley in Lincolnshire with a Väderstad cultivator drill.

Technical specification

Produced:	1987-93 (Ford livery from 1989)
Engine:	Cummins NTA-855-A360
Cylinders:	6 turbocharged/aftercooled
Bore x stroke:	5½in x 6in
Horsepower:	360hp
Rated speed:	2,100rpm
Transmission:	12 forward, 4 reverse constant mesh or 12 forward, 2 reverse power-shift
Hydraulics:	24.5gpm pump, 2,400psi
Lift capacity:	21,700lb (9,843kg)
Weight:	21,600lb (9,797kg)
Tyre sizes:	24.5x32

This 1990 Ford 976 Versatile, rated at 360hp, coupled to a 40ft John Deere air seeder was seen outside Denver, Colorado, planting winter wheat in a field more than a mile long. The operator claimed he could plant between 35 and 40 acres an hour when travelling at 6mph. Photo: Peter D Simpson.

Is it a Ford?

Scott Lambert plays spot the difference, when he finds the Ford 976 is similar to other tractors.

Ford had a history of using articulated tractors built by other companies and re-branding them – the FW Series based on a Steiger Panther III being a prime example. So, when it bought the Winnipeg-based Versatile company in 1987, it was inevitable that the striking red and yellow livery would give way to the blue, black and white of Ford New Holland.

Based heavily on the Versatile tractors available at the time, the blue tractor was badged as the Ford 976 Versatile – and it was clear to see that the tractor was not new technology! The styling of the old Versatile 895 had become slightly less austere, but the square lines of Versatile were clearly visible.

The 976 used the proven Cummins NTA-855 14-litre engine, with turbocharging and aftercooling producing 360hp at the flywheel and 290hp at the drawbar. The six-cylinder lump was good for 1,170lb ft of torque at 1,400rpm and was a common choice for manufacturers building tractors of this size.

Unlike some of its counterparts, the 976 was available with a three-point linkage using category IV links. Astonishingly, the tractor could lift more than it weighed itself!

Like all Versatile tractors that had gone before it, the 976 built a reputation for reliability and dependability, helping Ford New Holland to cement its position as a worthy contender in the high-horsepower sector.

Production of tractors in blue, black and white continued until 2000 and the Versatile name returned in 2001 after Buhler Industries, a Canadian manufacturer of farm equipment, bought the Winnipeg plant. ■

Key facts

Built:	Manitoba, Canada
Engine:	6-cyl Cummins NTA-855-A360
Power:	360hp
Chassis:	Articulated, four-wheel drive
Typical farm:	Large American arable

End of the trac

Mercedes-Benz's MB trac was unique but was not to last, as Howard Sherren discovers.

The Unimog was one of Mercedes-Benz's first attempts at attacking the agricultural and commercial markets and proved successful for those who wanted a farm vehicle and tractor in one. Its development led to a more tractor-based machine aimed mainly at farms and in 1972 the first MB trac arrived. It featured four large equal wheels with a centrally-mounted cab and rear load deck – a completely new concept to British farmers.

It now seems extremely dated with its angular design, manual controls and limited electronics compared to the JCB Fastrac, but at the time it carried cutting-edge technology with suspension and a high-speed gearbox – finding a place on many farms or in municipal applications.

As farms became larger so did tractors – and so did the MB trac. Starting with small 24in wheels on the 65 and 70 models, they had increased to 30in when the 1300 arrived in 1976 and were up to 34in on the 1500 in 1980. When the flagship 156hp 1600 Turbo was launched in 1987 it was fitted with 18.4

R34 rubber, making it extremely stable and dramatically improving its capabilities.

It found its way into many different operations across Britain, whether on large arable farms, used with a slurry tanker on stock farms or even in forestry.

The 1600 came fitted with a Mercedes OM366A engine that produced 156hp at 2,400rpm – the more power the better! It was a good performer, producing 530Nm of torque from the small bore, long stroke engine. The capacity of just under six litres wasn't the greatest; neither was the bore of 97.5mm, but the long stroke of 133mm

Built until 1991, the MB trac 1600 Turbo was the flagship tractor in the range until a few 1800 models were made at the end of production.

Left: A mixture of manual controls and levers is teamed with Bosch hydraulics to provide an effective system.

With the seat folded forward, the whole dashboard, pedals and control centre could be rotated 180 degrees in one piece on a sub-frame. As soon as this change was made the machine was ready to go in a matter of seconds. Also, because the cab was so enormous, the driver wasn't limited for space and access wasn't hindered.

The reverse drive was ideal for forager work, buck-raking on the silage clamp or with a logging trailer, even in the forest, making the tractor even more efficient and a pleasure to operate. Both front and rear windows opened wide and the door glass could be wound down as in a car.

Although not seen in Britain, a rear loader could be specified and mounted on the rear loading deck, turning the machine into a loading shovel. This loading deck could also be used for a seed hopper or, more commonly in Britain, a mounted sprayer tank.

Many of the smaller MB models were turned into self-propelled or forward control sprayers, but the larger versions were avoided because of their physical size and weight.

The rear linkage offered 6½ tonnes of lifting power, adequate for the heaviest of ploughs, cultivators and drills, whilst up-front the versatility was increased further with a three-tonne front linkage which was perfect for presses, cultivators, tanks and toppers.

Hydraulic capacity was pretty average at 55 litres per minute, which may have struggled to provide the maximum three front and four rear double-acting spool valves with a sufficient flow of oil.

Shoe brakes were fitted to each axle giving automotive stopping power and these were operated by the compressed ➡

kept it hanging in there when the going got tough.

Full-length side panels kept the powerplant well covered, but made

servicing a bit of a nightmare. Also, the enormous exhaust pipe with air pre-cleaner made forward visibility somewhat awkward.

With its four equal wheels, front and rear diff locks and front suspension with dampers, the tractor avoided shock loads from transport work and had excellent traction compared to the other non-equal wheeled machines on the market. Weight distribution, unladen, was 60 per cent front and 40 per cent rear, but this changed to 50:50 when an implement was attached to the three-point linkage.

The synchromesh gearbox offered as many as 16 forward and 16 reverse gears with an extra eight creeper speeds. This resulted in speeds from a crawling 0.29kph right up to 40kph – which was only just being offered by some other manufacturers.

Being a systems tractor, the MB trac offered a number of other unique features. Firstly, the machine could be ordered in reverse drive. Although some normal tractors could have this fitted, none were as easy as the MB to put into driving position.

Key facts

Built:	Baden-Baden, Germany
Engine:	6-cyl Mercedes-Benz OM366A
Power:	156hp
Chassis:	Rigid, four-wheel drive
Typical farm:	Large European arable

Access to the driver's seat is excellent: three generous steps lead up to the square, in-house-built cab of the MB trac 1600 Turbo.

The rear linkage was over-engineered and could cope with 6,500kg; a pick-up hitch is also attached.

Technical specification

Produced:	1987-91
Engine:	Mercedes-Benz OM366A
Cylinders:	6 turbocharged
Bore x stroke:	97.5mm x 133mm
Displacement:	5,958cc
Horsepower:	156hp @ 2,400rpm
Torque:	530Nm @ 1,500rpm
Transmission:	16 forward, 16 reverse
Speed range:	0.29kph – 40kph
Fuel capacity:	170 litres
Turning radius:	6,500mm
Length:	4,680mm
Weight (standard):	6,320kg
Tyre sizes:	18.4 R34

With just over 2,000 hours on the clock, this 1600 Turbo is in semi-retirement, as the cropped area has been considerably reduced.

air system fitted as standard to the tractors. Each new tractor was supplied with an airline for blowing out radiators and keeping tyres pumped up.

Weighing in at 6,320kg, all three models in the range could be loaded up to a gross vehicle weight of a whopping 10 tonnes.

This impressive machine wasn't to last, though, and Mercedes-Benz pulled the plug in 1991. But the design was taken by Trac-

Technik which went on to build the Trac 160, an improved version of the 1600 brought up-to-date from 1980s' technology.

Although no models were brought into Great Britain, the design was sold on to Doppstadt, which was renowned for its forestry machinery and started to sell the machine around the world, including the United Kingdom, at the beginning of the new millennium.

The bright orange machine looked far superior to the MB, with improved styling and controls in-line with modern-day competition. The build quality and reliability, however, were worse than the old models and the machine received bad press.

From the machines imported, which was under a dozen, only a few still remain in the country. After building about 600 machines Doppstadt ceased production of the model

Mercedes-Benz from Bruera Agricultural Ltd, whose salesman Tony Gerrard persuaded him to give the MB trac a try.

The MB trac 1600 was a rare machine in Britain, but Tony tracked down a demonstration model in Tadcaster, North Yorkshire, and then had to get it back quickly for the demonstration.

The only way was to drive it back to Merseyside, so he travelled up there on a Friday afternoon getting hold of the tractor about 5pm, then drove it back across the Pennines to Dave's yard (via the local chippy) in a total of four hours – not bad for a 90-mile journey.

But then it started raining and carried on for three days so no ploughing could be done and the machine couldn't be worked. On the Monday another MB dealer was on Dave's doorstep to take the tractor away for another demonstration. Dave wasn't impressed and Tony feared the deal was about to dissolve.

But he had one more trick up his sleeve. When a smaller demo MB trac 1000 became available he set about adding extra front ballast and hitching up Dave's six-furrow mounted plough to it. Amazingly, this 100hp machine not only lifted the plough but proceeded to work the field effortlessly.

That picture spoke a thousand words and everyone at Home Farm was extremely impressed: if this is what a 100hp is like, imagine the capabilities of the mighty 1600!

Dave recalls: "I had a number of tractors out on demonstration from local dealers but the MB was something special. I gave the choice to my workers as to which one we would buy, seeing as they would spend the most time on the machine, and the MB trac won hands down. The team described it as a man's tractor and it proved an extremely competent machine."

The demonstration 1600 Turbo which drove on to the farm briefly was set to make a return and the deal was agreed. The 1600, registered on a 'H' plate, must be one of the last machines made and the best surviving example with just 2,000 hours on the clock and original tyres.

The machine is fitted with reverse drive – although Dave hasn't found a use for it yet, it may be useful in the future.

The tractor proved to be perfect for hauling a vacuum tanker around during the 1990s, especially with its 40kph top speed and front suspension. They certainly made a great team – and spectacle – as they rumbled through the middle of Liverpool.

The tractor still remains the flagship on the farm and, although the cropping has been greatly reduced, it still has the odd trip out each year with the plough or on the heavy Rau discs for a spot of cultivation.

Dave still believes the MB trac is a quality piece of engineering and doubts he will ever part with it. ■

in 2004 to concentrate on its other forestry machines.

The smaller MB trac models were also produced by the Werner Company under the WF-Trac name: they are sold and serviced by the Unimog dealership network. The flagship WF-Trac 1700 is an incredible machine, which has a cab that can turn though 270 degrees and a Mercedes OM 904-LA engine producing 177hp.

One 1600 Turbo that made it into Britain (and is possibly the last machine sold) is that belonging to Dave Harrison from Hale in Merseyside, who farms the arable land north of the River Mersey and just south of Liverpool.

When he was looking for a new mainline ploughing tractor in the early 1990s, he considered a number of makes from local dealers, including Ford, John Deere and a

First and last

Howard Sherren looks at a mint example of the last crawler range to leave Track-Marshall's factory.

The rubber-tracked crawler market was dominated by one name in the late 1980s – Caterpillar with its Challenger 65.

Many were unsure the new idea would work, believing that the high horsepower the tracks would be subjected to would prematurely destroy them.

Caterpillar's Mobil-Trac system, however, used rubber tracks around steel cables that made them both strong and flexible and, once they had seen the system demonstrated, the Challenger's sheer pulling power and work-rate led many farmers to invest in it – and own a crawler that could be driven on the road and used in 'prairie-style' fields.

The 65 was launched at the 1989 Smithfield Show and awarded the RASE Gold medal in 1990 before receiving the RASE Silver medal in 1991.

But it was at the 1990 Royal Show that British farmers got their first glimpse of the TM 200, Track-Marshall's first and, unfortunately, last rubber-tracked crawler. Although the machine cost considerably more than many of the competing wheeled tractors at the time, its unique special features and versatility did create sales.

At its heart was a modified Australian-built Waltanna machine, which came with an improved cab and heavy-duty rear linkage.

Track-Marshall made modifications and improvements at its Gainsborough factory that enabled the crawler to meet regulations and be sold across Europe.

The TM 200 was revealed at the 1990 Royal Show and became available in April 1991. It provided competition for the Caterpillar 65 and had a host of features not offered by other manufacturers.

The first tractors were delivered in April 1991 and reports were very good, creating a stir at machinery demonstrations across the country. However, production didn't go as expected and less than two dozen tractors were ever modified by Track-Marshall: it is now unusual to find working examples in the country.

At least one machine was broken for spares (a great shame but at least it has kept the others tractors here in running order) but the majority are in the hands of collectors trying to save a piece of British engineering.

Recently a mint example changed hands. Having covered an amazingly low 1,000 hours, this TM 200 is as-new and joins a collection in Cambridgeshire. The unregistered model was used for a couple of years and parked up in the mind 1990s, then subsequently forgotten about in a shed. It sat for a number of years before being purchased by a well-known Marshall collector who subsequently let it go it to its current owners.

Front weights helped to ballast the 11½-tonne monster.

Key facts

Built:	Lincolnshire, UK
Engine:	6-cyl Cummins 6CT8.3
Power:	210hp
Chassis:	Rigid, rubber-tracked crawler
Typical farm:	Large British arable

After a bit of TLC, the years of dirt and dust were removed to restore it to its former glory and it looks amazing!

A 210hp Cummins 6CT8.3 propelled the TM 200, which was a change from the renowned Perkins units used on previous incarnations of Track-Marshall's steel-tracked crawlers.

The capacity was a huge 8.27 litres and the engine was also turbocharged to produce maximum power at a typical 2,200 rpm. A 114mm bore and 135mm stroke produced maximum torque at 1,500rpm. A few larger 250hp-engined versions were produced and badged the TM 250, but these models are even rarer.

Two Rexroth hydraulic motors provided the drive for the crawler and hydrostatic steering was obtained my adjusting the flow of oil to these rear-mounted units.

An infinitely variable transmission with two ranges provided speeds of up to just 13mph in forward and a steady 4.33mph in reverse.

A single joystick operated the transmission through a simple U-gate, pushing the lever forward on the left to move forwards and forward on the right for reverse.

The crawler had no need for brakes due to the transmission and engine braking. A button-operated parking brake provided added safety when stationary.

To adapt the crawler for the British market, a three-point linkage was required. A heavy-duty one was designed by Track-Marshall and it was capable of lifting an impressive

six tonnes to cater for most, if not all, arable operations. The design was similar to the company's existing steel-track crawlers but with extra metal providing more capacity.

The linkage featured some interesting features such as hydraulic rams as drop arms, giving the ability to lift each arm independently. This was very useful for hitching up implements and, in the field, adjusting implement height on uneven ➡

This multi-function joystick gave control over speed, direction and linkage.

Technical specification

Engine model:	Cummins 6CT8.3
Power:	210hp
Max power @:	2,200rpm
Max torque @:	1,500rpm
Cylinders:	6 turbocharged
Bore x stroke:	114mm x 135mm
Displacement:	8,270cc
Fuel capacity:	300 litres
Transmission:	Infinitely variable
Top speed:	13mph
Lift capacity:	6,000kg
Weight:	11,500kg
Track size:	510mm x 2,400mm
Cab:	TWR-designed

ground or raising one side higher than the other.

This feature, along with linkage height, was operated via push buttons on the control lever. The linkage also had the ability to sway from side to side, making turning with the implement in the ground a lot easier and causing less stress on the machine.

External linkage controls were also fitted to either side of the rear of the tractor, an unusual feature on tractors of this age. This gave control of height of linkage and furthermore the height of each individual lift ram.

A closed-centre hydraulic system providing 90 litres per minute was used on the TM 200. The system ran at 170 bar (2,500psi) and supplied the motors, linkage and spool valves.

Only two double-acting spool valves were fitted to the crawler, which was not ideal for arable operations where often three or more were required. They were electronically operated via rocker switches on the side console.

The hydraulics were known to be rather problematic due to the large amount of electric and hydraulic parts fitted to the machine. The pipes commonly failed and oil was known to overheat – in many cases this was due to poor cooling capabilities.

A 1,000rpm pto was also fitted for versatility.

Ground clearance was also an issue with the crawler as it was only a few inches off the ground which meant tough going on uneven land.

The positively-driven tracks were 510mm wide by 2,400mm long, which gave a ground pressure of just 0.45 Bar. This was excellent for a machine that weighed a massive 11½ tonnes.

Greater traction was also achieved because of their larger contact area than that offered by tyres and, combined with the weight, reduced the slip to just two or three per cent.

However, the tracks weren't capable of handling the TM 200's power and failed quickly. The positive drive meant that the

Now in the safe hands of a collector, this TM 200 has covered just 1,000 hours in its relatively-short life.

Left: No pedals meant the TWR-designed cab was spacious and uncluttered.

The cab design was down to the TWR Group which was better known for the design of the Jaguar XJ220 super car.

Track-Marshall was an industrial division of the TWR Group at the time of production and a decision was made to let the specialist design team work its wonders on the TM 200.

The cab was extremely spacious and fitted with tinted glass, air conditioning and a fully-adjustable and swivel-mounted seat, making it an extremely comfortable working environment.

An absence of foot pedals meant extra leg space for the taller drivers and enough space for a few passengers!

The dashboard featured a combination of digital and analogue dials – ground, pto and engine speed and engine hours were all shown digitally, while oil pressure, fuel level, battery voltage, water temperature and air pressure had analogue gauges.

The cab conveniently lifted and pivoted via a hand-operated ram to enable access to the maze of hydraulic pipes and pump located underneath it. All it took was just two bolts and extending a ram to access the vital parts for repair. It was simple and very effective.

It is such a shame that this unique machine didn't make it into the future and that the Linconshire-based Track-Marshall company was consigned to the history books. The TM 200 had a host of unique features that haven't been seen on agricultural tractors since that time.

At least mint examples, such as this one, are being kept in working order by collectors to show off British engineering at its best. ■

lugs suffered incredible stresses in heavy ground conditions because the solid steel drive wheels did not allow much movement or play.

Tracks were commonly failing before they were worn out on nearly all machines, and they weren't cheap at around £7,000 a set.

Most users converted their TM 200 to run on Cat tracks and running gear when the original gear broke or the tracks wore out. This involved modifying the rear drive wheels, moving the track tensioning ram forward to accommodate the larger wheels and lowering the air bags to enable them to operate correctly.

The Caterpillar tracks were more readily available, lasted longer, were more cost-efficient and provided a smoother ride from the suspended front axle and rubber front tyres. An adjustable centre idler wheel also provided extra movement.

The rear linkage was designed and built by Track-Marshall and could cope with six tonnes.